Bookkeeping 2

Workbook

David Cox
Michael Fardon

AAT WISE GUIDES – for convenient exam revision

This handy pocket-sized guide provides the **perfect study and revision resource** for the AAT Level 2 Certificate in Accounting.

available for:

Bookkeeping 1
Bookkeeping 2
Working in Accounting and Finance
Introduction to Costing

Visit www.osbornebooks.co.uk for further information and to place your order.

Published by Osborne Books Limited
Unit 1B Everoak Estate
Bromyard Road, Worcester WR2 5HP
Tel 01905 748071
Email books@osbornebooks.co.uk
Website www.osbornebooks.co.uk

Design by Laura Ingham

Printed by CPI Group (UK) Limited, Croydon, CR0 4YY, on environmentally friendly, acid-free paper from managed forests.

MIX
Paper from
responsible sources
FSC® C013604

British Library Cataloguing in Publication Data
A catalogue record for this book is available from the British Library

ISBN 978 1909173 057

Contents

Introduction

Chapter activities

Chapter activities – answers

Practice assessments – tasks

Practice assessments – answers

Acknowledgements

The publisher wishes to thank the following for their help with the reading and production of the book: Maz Loton and Cathy Turner. Thanks are also due to Debbie Board for contributing a significant amount of new assessment material, to Hania Lee for her technical reading and to Laura Ingham for her designs for this series.

The publisher is indebted to the Association of Accounting Technicians for its help and advice to our authors and editors during the preparation of this text.

Authors

David Cox has more than twenty years' experience teaching accountancy students over a wide range of levels. Formerly with the Management and Professional Studies Department at Worcester College of Technology, he now lectures on a freelance basis and carries out educational consultancy work in accountancy studies. He is author and joint author of a number of textbooks in the areas of accounting, finance and banking.

Michael Fardon has extensive teaching experience of a wide range of banking, business and accountancy courses at Worcester College of Technology. He now specialises in writing business and financial texts and is General Editor at Osborne Books. He is also an educational consultant and has worked extensively in the areas of vocational business curriculum development.

Introduction

what this book covers

This book has been written to cover the Unit 'Control accounts, journals and the banking system' which is mandatory for the revised (2013) AAT Level 2 Certificate in Accounting.

what this book contains

This book is set out in two sections:

■ **Chapter Activities** which provide extra practice material in addition to the activities included in the Osborne Books Tutorial text. Answers to the Chapter activities are included in this book.

■ **Practice Assessments** are provided to prepare the student for the Computer Based Assessments. They are based directly on the structure, style and content of the sample assessment material provided by the AAT at www.aat.org.uk. Suggested answers to the Practice Assessments are set out in this book.

further information

If you want to know more about our products and resources, please visit www.osbornebooks.co.uk for further details and access to our online shop.

Chapter
activities

1 Banks, building societies and payment systems

1.1 Banks and building societies offer many similar services, but there are some services which the smaller building societies do not offer.

From the list below tick the services that are offered by banks and/or small building societies.

Service	Offered by banks ✔	Offered by small building societies ✔
Debit card		
Business loans		
Personal current account		
House mortgage		
Leasing		
Savings accounts		
Investments		
Insurance		
Personal loan		

1.2 When a customer pays in a cheque to a bank, the customer is safe to withdraw the amount of that cheque after:

	✔
2 working days	
4 working days	
6 working days	

1.3   Banking documents should normally be retained for a period of at least:

	✔
One year	
Six years	
Eight years	

Select the correct option.

1.4   A dishonoured cheque is:

	✔
A cheque that has been refused by the person to whom it is made payable	
A cheque that a customer has issued but the bank refuses to pay	
A cheque that a customer has refused to issue because the goods supplied are faulty	

Select the correct option.

1.5   A prepayment card is:

	✔
A card which can be purchased by a customer and has an amount programmed in which the customer can use up by making purchases	
A card issued to a customer which enables the customer to make purchases and pay for them later	
A card only issued to customers over 18 which enables them to make purchases overseas	

Select the correct option.

2 Making payments

2.1 A business will need to carry out a series of internal checks and procedures before making a payment to a supplier.

Indicate from the following list the checks and procedures that will normally be needed before a payment is made to a supplier. State 'yes' or 'no'.

Check or procedure	Yes ✔	No ✔
Documents (eg purchase order, delivery note, invoice) checked against each other to make sure they tie up		
Any credit due has been acknowledged in the form of a credit note		
Any remittance advice due has been received		
Any discounts due have been allowed by the supplier		
All invoices have been given at least 30 days credit		
Payment authorisation has been given		

2.2 A bank giro credit can be used in order to:

	✔
Make payment of a bill direct to a bank account	
Advise a supplier that a payment has been sent to a bank account	
Obtain cash from the bank to pay wages	

Select the correct option.

2.3   A BACS direct credit is normally used in order to:

✔

Pay bank charges	
Make payments to suppliers	
Pay insurance premiums	

Choose the correct option.

2.4   You have been asked to set up a Standing Order authority, using the details set out below. You will not have to sign it or date it. Your business and bank details are already on the form.

> Hunter Limited: Office Rental Payments
>
> 12 monthly instalments of £1,500.00 to Ace Properties from 15 January 20-4, under reference EE1934.
>
> Bank details Ventura Bank, Persham, Sort Code 69 98 15, Account 34512358.

STANDING ORDER MANDATE

To _____Mercia_____ Bank

Address 45 Market Street, Persham, PE4 8CV _____

PLEASE PAY TO

Bank _____   Branch _____   Sort code [   ]

Beneficiary _____   Account number [   ]

The sum of £ [   ]   Amount in words _____

Date of first payment _____   Frequency of payment _____

Until _____   Reference _____

Account to be debited Hunter Limited   Account number 22472434

SIGNATURE(S)   ....

---

3   Receiving and recording payments

3.1   A business receiving cash for sales that it has made operates a cash till.

At the end of each working day the cash in the till is counted and a certain amount is kept in the till as a 'float' and the rest paid into the bank on paying-in slip.

On Monday the cashier noted the following details:

	£	£
Cash float in the till at the beginning of the day		275.00
Cash receipts from sales during the day:	25.00	
	19.65	
	76.40	
	32.50	
	67.95	
	125.90	
	4.50	
Cash taken from the cash till for paying in at the bank		380.90

Answer the following questions:

(a)   What was the total of the cash received during the day?

(b)   What was the total of the cash in the till at the end of the day before the cash for paying in at the bank was taken out?

(c)   What was the total of the cash float held overnight on Monday?

3.2 You work for Tandem Limited and deal with cheques received from customers. Part of your job is to check the cheques and either pass them forward for listing and paying in at the bank or query them.

During the course of Monday 20 October 20-4 you receive a cheque which you think may cause a problem.

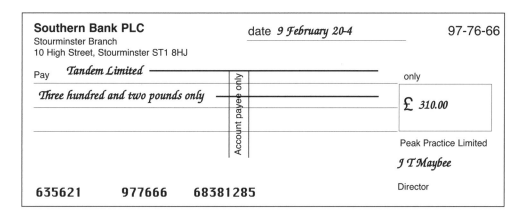

State two reasons why this cheque should not be paid into the bank.

(a)

(b)

3.3 'Chargeback' in relation to a card payment means that

		✔
The purchaser who receives faulty or incorrect goods bought using a debit or credit card can claim back the amount paid		
A business selling goods online is entitled to deduct postage and packing charges from the purchaser's account if a debit card is used		

Select the correct option.

3.4 When an online trader accepts debit and credit card payments, the customer fills in an online order form and provides details, including:

	✔
Date of birth, card number, security code	
Date of birth, card number, expiry date	
Card number, expiry date, security code	

Which **ONE** of these options is correct?

3.5 A business receives a remittance advice (shown below) which is unfortunately incomplete.

TO	REMITTANCE ADVICE	FROM
Bristol Street Supplies 67 Bristol Street Bartfield BA6 7TY	2 December 20-4	**Helford Ltd** **16 Kent Road** **Manorfield** **MA2 6GP**

date	your reference	our reference	payment amount
03 11 -4	INVOICE 10956	3213	700.00
15 11 -4	INVOICE 11024	3287	325.95
20 11 -4	CREDIT NOTE 167	3287	(45.60)
		TOTAL	

(a) What should the total figure be?

(b) There are two common methods of sending money in settlement of accounts. Select from the following list: BACS/Faster payments, Cash, Debit card, Credit card, Cheque, CHAPS.

(c) Which method is most likely to have been used in this case, bearing in mind the details shown on the remittance advice?

4 Paying into the bank

4.1 The cheque shown below has to be paid into the bank.

There are a number of problems with the cheque.

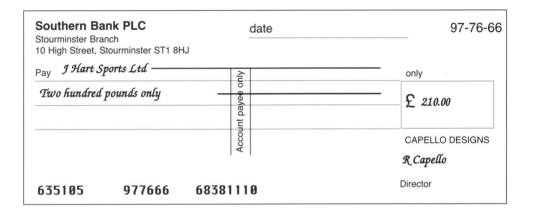

What action would you need to take in the following circumstances:

(a) The amount in words and figures is different

(b) There is no date on the cheque

4.2 You work for Plumstead Traders Limited, which has a bank account at Central Bank, Persham. You are required to prepare the paying-in slip and counterfoil as at today's date. The cheques are to be listed and totalled on the back of the paying-in slip. The items to be banked are:

Cash	Cheques	
three £20 notes	£60.00	Balkan Enterprises
six £10 notes	£65.60	Mindwell Catering
two £5 notes	£99.95	C Harrison & Co
four £1 coins	£24.00	H Richter
two 50p coins		
four 10p coins		
three 2p coins		

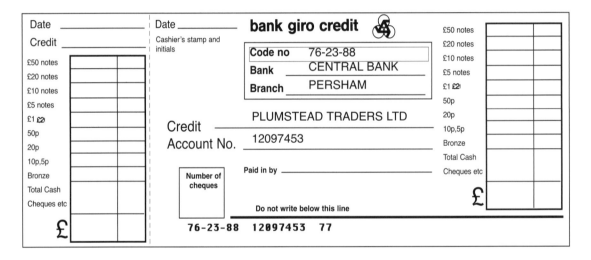

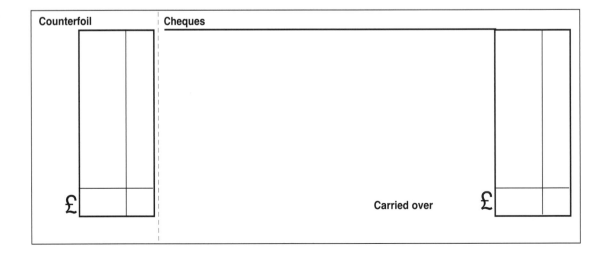

4.3   You work for Butterworth Ltd, which has a bank account at Albion Bank, Broadfield. Butterworth Ltd has an online shop. You have just received the December bank statement, which is shown below. Study the statement and answer the questions that follow.

Albion Bank plc
7 The Avenue, Broadfield, BR1 2AJ

	Account title	Butterworth
	Account number	15239524
	Statement	15

Date	Details	Payments	Receipts	Balance
20-4				
3 Dec	Balance brought down			1,750.00 CR
8 Dec	BACS Credit D Guest		3,430.00	5,180.00 CR
12 Dec	DD Wyvern Insurance	260.60		4,919.40 CR
12 Dec	526147	150.00		4,769.40 CR
14 Dec	526148	67.45		4,701.95 CR
15 Dec	Websales 24237942		2,960.00	7,661.95 CR
16 Dec	SO Granby Finance	680.00		6,981.95 CR
16 Dec	Giro Credit 92842		1,195.60	8,177.55 CR
22 Dec	BACS Payroll	4,127.00		4,050.55 CR
24 Dec	Bank Charges	490.70		3,559.85 CR

(a)   Explain how the payment received on 8 December is made to the bank.

(b)   Explain the payment received on 15 December.

(c)   If the payment into the bank received on 16 December had contained a cheque for £350 which was then dishonoured and sent back to Albion Bank, what would the balance of the bank account have been on 24 December?

5 Bank reconciliation statements

5.1 Upon receipt of a bank statement, which **ONE** of the following must be written into the firm's cash book?

	✔
Payment debited in error by the bank	
Unpresented cheques	
BACS transfers from customers	
Outstanding lodgements	

5.2 A firm's bank statement shows an overdraft of £600. Unpresented cheques total £250; outstanding lodgements total £1,000. What is the balance at bank shown by the cash book?

	✔
£150 debit	
£650 debit	
£250 credit	
£150 credit	

5.3   Show whether the following statements are true or false.

Statement		True ✔	False ✔
(a)	Some differences between the bank statement and the cash book are described as timing differences – these are not corrected in the cash book		
(b)	A trade receivable's cheque has been dishonoured and returned by the bank – the amount of the returned cheque must be recorded in cash book on the debit side		
(c)	In a bank reconciliation statement which starts with the balance as per bank statement, unpresented cheques are deducted		
(d)	The opening cash book balance at bank will always be the same as the opening bank statement balance		

5.4   On 30 June Martinez & Co received the following bank statement as at 27 June 20-4.

BANK STATEMENT				
Date **20-4**	**Details**	**Paid out** £	**Paid in** £	**Balance** £
01 Jun	Balance brought forward			2,685 C
02 Jun	Cheque 784342	855		1,830 C
07 Jun	BACS credit: P Parker		1,525	3,355 C
08 Jun	Cheque 784344	697		2,658 C
10 Jun	Cheque 784345	1,922		736 C
14 Jun	Paid into bank		2,607	3,343 C
15 Jun	Cheque 784343	412		2,931 C
18 Jun	BACS credit: Watson Ltd		2,109	5,040 C
24 Jun	Direct debit: First Electric	112		4,928 C
24 Jun	Cheque 784347	1,181		3,747 C
25 Jun	Bank charges	45		3,702 C
26 Jun	Cheque 784348	594		3,108 C
D = Debit C = Credit				

The cash book as at 27 June 20-4 is shown below.

CASH BOOK

Date 20-4	Details	Bank £	Date 20-4	Cheque number	Details	Bank £
01 Jun	Balance b/f	1,830	03 Jun	784343	Gladysz & Co	412
05 Jun	P Parker	1,525	03 Jun	784344	Daley Ltd	697
10 Jun	Dunlevy Ltd	2,607	03 Jun	784345	Ward & Lamb	1,922
25 Jun	Corline Traders	1,433	12 Jun	784346	Hendrie Stores	692
26 Jun	Moss & Co	786	12 Jun	784347	McCabes	1,181
			12 Jun	784348	Rehman Ltd	594
			24 Jun		First Electric	112
			25 Jun	784349	Hannaford & Co	764

(a) Check the items on the bank statement against the items in the cash book.

(b) Enter any items in the cash book as needed.

(c) Total the cash book and clearly show the balance carried down at 27 June (closing balance) and brought down at 28 June (opening balance).

Select your entries for the Details column from the following list: Balance b/f, Balance c/d, Bank charges, Closing balance, Corline Traders, Daley Ltd, Dunlevy Ltd, First Electric, Gladysz & Co, Hannaford & Co, Hendrie Stores, McCabes, Moss & Co, Opening balance, P Parker, Rehman Ltd, Ward & Lamb, Watson Ltd.

(d) Complete the bank reconciliation statement as at 27 June.

Select your entries for the Details column from the following list: Bank charges, Corline Traders, Daley Ltd, Dunlevy Ltd, First Electric, Gladysz & Co, Hannaford & Co, Hendrie Stores, McCabes, Moss & Co, P Parker, Rehman Ltd, Ward & Lamb, Watson Ltd.

Bank reconciliation statement as at 27 June 20-4	
Balance as per bank statement	£
Add	
Name:	£
Name:	£
Total to add	£
Less	
Name:	£
Name:	£
Total to subtract	£
Balance as per cash book	£

6 Using control accounts

6.1 You have the following information for the month:

•	customer balances at start of month	£25,685
•	credit sales	£18,732
•	sales returns	£876
•	money received from customers	£17,455
•	discounts allowed	£227
•	irrecoverable debt written off	£175

What is the figure for customer balances at the end of the month?

	✔
£23,130	
£25,684	
£25,686	
£26,034	

6.2 You have the following information for the month:

•	supplier balances at start of month	£13,278
•	credit purchases	£9,584
•	purchases returns	£821
•	money paid to suppliers	£10,058
•	discounts received	£247

What is the figure for supplier balances at the end of the month?

	✔
£12,230	
£13,378	
£11,736	
£14,820	

6.3 You have the following information for the month:

- balance of VAT account at start of month   £2,380   credit
- VAT from sales day book   £1,420
- VAT from purchases day book   £1,065
- VAT from sales returns day book   £223
- VAT from purchases returns day book   £185
- VAT from cash sales   £592

What is the balance of VAT account at the end of the month?

	✔
£1,471 debit	
£1,471 credit	
£3,289 debit	
£3,289 credit	

6.4 You work as an accounts assistant for Tilsley Trading. Today you are working on the purchases ledger control account and purchases ledger.

A summary of transactions with credit suppliers during the month of June is shown below.

(a) Show whether each entry will be a debit or a credit in the purchases ledger control account in the general ledger.

Details	Amount £	Debit ✔	Credit ✔
Balance of credit suppliers at 1 June	35,106		
Purchases from credit suppliers	20,354		
Payments to credit suppliers	19,062		
Discounts received	289		
Goods returned to credit suppliers	1,374		

(b) What will be the balance brought down on 1 July on the above account?

	✔
Dr £34,735	
Cr £34,735	
Dr £35,477	
Cr £35,477	
Dr £35,313	
Cr £35,313	

The following credit balances were in the purchases ledger on 1 July.

	£
Cockerill Ltd	9,262
Darnbrook & Co	3,495
M Warren	5,724
De Graaf Ltd	6,098
Hannaford Trading	4,477
Quesne plc	5,386

(c) Reconcile the balances shown above with the purchases ledger control account balance calculated in part (b).

	£
Balance on purchases ledger control account at 30 June	
Total of the purchases ledger balances at 30 June	
Difference	

(d) What may have caused the difference you calculated in part (c)?

	✔
Settlement (cash) discount was entered twice in the purchases ledger control account	
A credit note was not entered in the purchases ledger control account	
A credit note was not entered in the purchases ledger	
Settlement (cash) discount was not entered in the purchases ledger	

(e) Which **ONE** of the following statements is true?

	✔
Reconciliation of the purchases ledger control account assures managers that the amount showing as outstanding to trade payables is correct	
Reconciliation of the purchases ledger control account assures managers that the amount showing as outstanding from trade receivables is correct	
Reconciliation of the purchases ledger control account will show if a sales invoice has been omitted from the purchases ledger	
Reconciliation of the purchases ledger control account will show if a sales invoice has been omitted from the sales ledger	

6.5   You work as an accounts assistant for Craven Cottages Ltd. Today you are working on the VAT control account.

The following figures have been taken from Craven Cottages' books of prime entry:

Totals for quarter

Sales day book	
Net	£68,800
VAT	£13,760
Gross	£82,560

Purchases day book	
Net	£35,600
VAT	£7,120
Gross	£42,720

Sales returns day book	
Net	£2,240
VAT	£448
Gross	£2,688

Purchases returns day book	
Net	£1,640
VAT	£328
Gross	£1,968

Cash book: cash-sales	
Net	£2,840
VAT	£568
Gross	£3,408

(a)   What will be the entries in the VAT control account to record the VAT transactions in the quarter?

Select your entries for the Details columns from the following list: Cash sales, Purchases, Purchases day book, Purchases returns, Purchases returns day book, Sales, Sales day book, Sales returns, Sales returns day book, Value Added Tax.

VAT control account

Details	Amount £	Details	Amount £

(b)   The VAT Return has been completed and shows an amount owing to HM Revenue & Customs of £6,432.

Is the VAT Return correct?

	✔
Yes	
No	

7 The journal

7.1 Which **ONE** of the following transactions will be recorded in the journal?

	✔
Purchase of goods on credit	
Payroll transactions	
Goods returned by a credit customer	
Sale of goods for cash	

7.2 Mohammed Pazir started in business on 1 February 20-4 with the following assets and liabilities:

	£
Vehicle	6,500
Fixtures and fittings	2,800
Inventory	4,100
Cash	150
Bank	1,250
Loan from uncle	5,000

Use the form below to prepare Mohammed's opening journal entry, showing clearly his capital at 1 February 20-4.

Date 20-4	Details	Reference	Dr £	Cr £

7.3 You are employed by Sachdev Supplies as an accounts assistant. Today the accounts supervisor tells you that a credit customer, Lefroy Limited, has ceased trading, owing Sachdev Supplies £560 plus VAT at 20%.

(a) Record the journal entries needed in the general ledger to write off the net amount and the VAT.

Select your account names from the following list: Irrecoverable debts, Lefroy Limited, Purchases, Purchases ledger control, Sachdev Supplies, Sales, Sales ledger control, Value Added Tax.

Account name	Amount £	Debit ✔	Credit ✔

(b) Sachdev Supplies has started a new business, Sachdev Developments, and a new set of accounts is to be opened. A partially completed journal to record the opening entries is shown below.

Record the journal entries needed in the accounts in the general ledger of Sachdev Developments to deal with the opening entries.

Account name	Amount £	Debit ✔	Credit ✔
Sales ledger control	14,275		
Purchases ledger control	7,392		
Inventory	4,107		
Office equipment	10,400		
Cash at bank	2,822		
Rent and rates	4,086		
Miscellaneous expenses	794		
Wages	2,397		
Loan from bank	6,250		
Capital	25,239		
Journal to record the opening entries of the new business			

7.4   You are employed by Mullen Limited as an accounts assistant.

Mullen Limited pays its employees through the bank every month and maintains a wages control account. A summary of last month's payroll transactions is shown below.

Item	£
Gross wages	22,352
Income tax	2,510
Employer's National Insurance contributions	1,105
Employees' National Insurance contributions	965
Employer's pension contributions	1,032
Employees' pension contributions	1,032

Record the journal entries needed in the general ledger to:

(a)   Record the wages expense.

(b)   Record HM Revenue & Customs liability.

(c)   Record the net wages paid to the employees.

(d)   Record the pension fund liability.

Select your account names from the following list: Bank, Employees' National Insurance, Employer's National Insurance, HM Revenue & Customs, Income tax, Net wages, Pension fund, Wages control, Wages expense.

(a)

Account name	Amount £	Debit ✔	Credit ✔

(b)

Account name	Amount £	Debit ✔	Credit ✔

(c)

Account name	Amount £	Debit ✔	Credit ✔

(d)

Account name	Amount £	Debit ✔	Credit ✔

8 The trial balance and correction of errors

8.1 Fill in the missing words from the following sentences, choosing from:

omission   commission   principle   original entry   reversal of entries   compensating

(a) "You made an error of .... when you debited the cost of diesel fuel for the van to Vans Account."

(b) "I've had an email from the accounts supervisor at Jones Limited concerning the statements of account that we sent out the other day. She says that there is a sales invoice charged that she knows nothing about. I wonder if it should be for T Jones' account and we have made an error of ....?"

(c) "There is a 'bad figure' on a purchases invoice – we have read it as £35 when it should be £55. It has gone through our accounts wrongly so we have an error of .... to put right."

(d) "Although the trial balance balanced last week, I've since found an error of £100 in the calculation of the balance of sales account. We will need to check the other balances as I think we may have a .... error."

(e) "Who was in charge of that trainee last week? He has entered the payment for the electricity bill on the debit side of the bank and on the credit side of electricity – a ...."

(f) "I found this purchase invoice from last week in amongst the copy statements. As we haven't put it through the accounts we have an error of ...."

8.2 Telephone expenses of £250 paid from the bank have been debited to the bank columns of the cash book and credited to the telephone expenses account. Which one of the following entries will correct the error?

Debit		Credit		✔
Bank	£250	Telephone expenses	£250	
Telephone expenses	£250	Bank	£250	
Bank	£250	Telephone expenses	£250	
Bank	£250	Telephone expenses	£250	
Telephone expenses	£250	Bank	£250	
Telephone expenses	£250	Bank	£250	

8.3 The trial balance of Tairo Traders does not balance. The debit column totals £220,472 and the credit column totals £217,647.

(a) What entry will be made in the suspense account to balance the trial balance?

Account name	Amount £	Debit ✔	Credit ✔
Suspense			

It is important to understand the type of errors that are disclosed by a trial balance and those that are not.

(b) Show which of the errors below are, or are not, disclosed by the trial balance.

Error in the general ledger	Error disclosed by the trial balance ✔	Error NOT disclosed by the trial balance ✔
The cost of diesel fuel, £50, has been debited in the cash book and credited to vehicles account		
A credit sale of £225 has not been entered in the accounts		
The balance of wages account has been calculated incorrectly		
A cash purchase of £85 has been recorded in the cash book only		
The cost of stationery, £54, has been recorded as £45 in the cash book and stationery account		
Rent paid of £450 has been debited to rent paid account and debited in the cash book		

8.4   The initial trial balance of Merrett Marketing at 30 June 20-3 did not balance. The difference of £371 was placed into a suspense account.

The error has been traced to the purchases day book as shown below.

Purchases day book

Date 20-3	Details	Invoice number	Total £	VAT £	Net £
30 Jun	Downing Traders	2798	720	120	600
30 Jun	Morwenna and Co	M/2348	576	96	480
30 Jun	Oades plc	4592	1,248	208	1,040
	Totals		2,120	424	2,120

(a)   Identify the error and record the journal entries needed in the general ledger to:

(1)   Remove the incorrect entry.

(2)   Record the correct entry.

(3)   Remove the suspense account balance.

Select your account name from the following list: Downing Traders, Morwenna and Co, Oades plc, Purchases, Purchases day book, Purchases ledger control, Purchases returns, Purchases returns day book, Sales, Sales day book, Sales ledger control, Sales returns, Sales returns day book, Suspense, Value Added Tax.

(1)

Account name	Amount £	Debit ✔	Credit ✔

(2)

Account name	Amount £	Debit ✔	Credit ✔

(3)

Account name	Amount £	Debit ✔	Credit ✔

An entry to record a bank payment of £525 for rent paid has been reversed.

(b) Record the journal entries needed in the general ledger to:

(1) Remove the incorrect entry.

(2) Record the correct entry.

Select your account names from the following list: Bank, Cash, Purchases, Purchases ledger control, Rent, Sales, Sales ledger control, Suspense, Value Added Tax.

(1)

Account name	Amount £	Debit ✔	Credit ✔

(2)

Account name	Amount £	Debit ✔	Credit ✔

8.5 The trial balance of Fayer and Co included a suspense account. All the bookkeeping errors have now been traced and the journal entries shown below have been recorded.

Journal entries

Account name	Debit £	Credit £
Office expenses	180	
Office equipment		180
Sales returns	295	
Suspense		295
Vehicle expenses	350	
Suspense		350

As the accounts assistant at Fayer and Co, you are to post the journal entries to the general ledger accounts. Dates are not required.

Select your entries for the Details column from the following list: Balance b/f, Office equipment, Office expenses, Sales returns, Suspense, Vehicle expenses.

Office expenses Account

Details	Amount £	Details	Amount £

Office equipment Account

Details	Amount £	Details	Amount £

Sales returns Account

Details	Amount £	Details	Amount £

Suspense Account

Details	Amount £	Details	Amount £
Balance b/f	645		

Vehicle expenses Account

Details	Amount £	Details	Amount £

8.6 On 30 June 20-9 Khela Krafts extracted an initial trial balance which did not balance, and a suspense account was opened. On 1 July journal entries were prepared to correct the errors that had been found, and to clear the suspense account. The list of balances in the initial trial balance, and the journal entries to correct the errors, are shown below and on the next page.

As the accounts assistant at Khela Krafts, you are to redraft the trial balance by placing the figures in the debit or credit column. You should take into account the journal entries (on the next page) which will clear the suspense account.

Account name	Balances extracted on 30 June 20-9	Balances at 1 July 20-9	
	£	Debit £	Credit £
Inventory	8,692		
Sales ledger control	12,347		
Petty cash control	84		
Capital	15,287		
Loan from bank	8,625		
VAT owing to HM Revenue & Customs	2,733		
Purchases ledger control	8,421		
Bank (cash at bank)	1,596		
Sales	77,364		
Sales returns	2,913		
Purchases	40,467		
Purchases returns	872		
Wages	20,644		
Advertising	2,397		
Insurance	1,849		
Heating and lighting	1,066		
Rent and rates	3,862		
Vehicle expenses	2,035		
Vehicles	15,400		
Suspense account (credit balance)	50		
Totals			

Journal entries

Account name	Debit £	Credit £
Suspense	490	
Purchases returns		490

Account name	Debit £	Credit £
Suspense	320	
Vehicle expenses		320
Vehicle expenses	230	
Suspense		230

Account name	Debit £	Credit £
Advertising	530	
Suspense		530

for your notes

Chapter activities answers

1   Banks, building societies and payment systems

1.1

Service	Offered by banks	Offered by small building societies
Debit card	✔	✔
Business loans	✔	
Personal current account	✔	✔
House mortgage	✔	✔
Leasing	✔	
Savings accounts	✔	✔
Investments	✔	✔
Insurance	✔	✔
Personal loan	✔	✔

1.2   6 working days

1.3   Six years

1.4   A cheque that a customer has issued but the bank refuses to pay

1.5   A card which can be purchased by a customer and has an amount programmed in which the customer can use up by making purchases

2   Making payments

2.1

Check or procedure	Yes	No
Documents (eg purchase order, delivery note, invoice) checked against each other to make sure they tie up	✔	
Any credit due has been acknowledged in the form of a credit note	✔	
Any remittance advice due has been received		✔
Any discounts due have been allowed by the supplier	✔	
All invoices have been given at least 30 days credit		✔
Payment authorisation has been given	✔	

2.2   Make payment of a bill direct to a bank account

2.3   Make payments to suppliers

2.4

STANDING ORDER MANDATE

To ___Mercia_____ Bank

Address __45 Market Street, Persham, PE4 8CV_____

PLEASE PAY TO

Bank __Ventura_____ Branch __Persham_____ Sort code | 69 98 15 |

Beneficiary __Ace Properties_____ Account number | 34512358 |

The sum of | £ 1,500.00 | Amount in words __one thousand five hundred pounds only__

Date of first payment __15 January 20-4_____ Frequency of payment __15th Monthly_____

Until __15 December 20-4_____ Reference __EE1934_____

Account to be debited | Hunter Limited | Account number | 22472434 |

SIGNATURE(S) ....

---

3 Receiving and recording payments

3.1 **(a)** £351.90

(b) £626.90

(c) £246.00

3.2 **(a)** The cheque is out of date

(b) The amount in words and figures is different

3.3 'Chargeback' in relation to a card payment means that the purchaser who receives faulty or incorrect goods bought using a debit or credit card can claim back the amount paid.

3.4 Card number, expiry date, security code

3.5 **(a)** £980.35

(b) BACS/Faster payments, Cheque

(c) Cheque - there are no bank details for the money transfer

4 Paying into the bank

4.1 **(a)** The cheque will need to be returned to the issuer, Capello Designs, and the incorrect amount altered and initialled or signed by the issuer.

(b) The date can be completed by the business paying in the cheque.

4.2 Total of cash £135.46

Total of cheques £249.55

Total of credit £385.01

4.3 **(a)** This payment for £3,430 is a BACS direct credit received from D Guest. It is paid direct to the bank account by computer transfer.

(b) This payment for £2,960 is likely to be receipts from sales on Butterworth Ltd's online shop, paid direct to the bank account.

(c) £3,209.85 CR

5 Bank reconciliation statements

5.1 BACS transfers from customers

5.2 £150 debit

5.3

	Statement	True	False
(a)	Some differences between the bank statement and the cash book are described as timing differences – these are not corrected in the cash book	✔	
(b)	A trade receivable's cheque has been dishonoured and returned by the bank – the amount of the returned cheque must be recorded in cash book on the debit side		✔
(c)	In a bank reconciliation statement which starts with the balance as per bank statement, unpresented cheques are deducted	✔	
(d)	The opening cash book balance at bank will always be the same as the opening bank statement balance		✔

5.4   (a) – (c)

CASH BOOK

Date 20-4	Details	Bank £	Date 20-4	Cheque	Details number	Bank £
01 Jun	Balance b/f	1,830	03 Jun	784343	Gladysz & Co	412
05 Jun	P Parker	1,525	03 Jun	784344	Daley Ltd	697
10 Jun	Dunlevy Ltd	2,607	03 Jun	784345	Ward & Lamb	1,922
25 Jun	Corline Traders	1,433	12 Jun	784346	Hendrie Stores	692
26 Jun	Moss & Co	786	12 Jun	784347	McCabes	1,181
18 Jun	Watson Ltd	2,109	12 Jun	784348	Rehman Ltd	594
			24 Jun		First Electric	112
			25 Jun	784349	Hannaford & Co	764
			25 Jun		Bank charges	45
			27 Jun		Balance c/d	3,871
		10,290				10,290
28 Jun	Balance b/d	3,871				

(d)

Bank reconciliation statement as at 27 June 20-4	
Balance as per bank statement	£3,108
Add	
Name: Corline Traders	£1,433
Name: Moss & Co	£786
Total to add	£2,219
Less	
Name: Hendrie Stores	£692
Name: Hannaford & Co	£764
Total to subtract	£1,456
Balance as per cash book	£3,871

6   Using control accounts

6.1   £25,684

6.2   £11,736

6.3   £3,289 credit

6.4

(a)

Details	Amount £	Debit	Credit
Balance of credit suppliers at 1 June	35,106		✔
Purchases from credit suppliers	20,354		✔
Payments to credit suppliers	19,062	✔	
Discounts received	289	✔	
Goods returned to credit suppliers	1,374	✔	

(b)

Cr £34,735	✔

(c)

	£
Balance on purchases ledger control account at 30 June	34,735
Total of the purchases ledger balances at 30 June	34,442
Difference	293

(d)

A credit note was not entered in the purchases ledger control account	✔

(e)

Reconciliation of the purchases ledger control account assures managers that the amount showing as outstanding to trade payables is correct	✔

6.5   (a)

VAT control Account

Details	Amount £	Details	Amount £
Purchases	7,120	Sales	13,760
Sales returns	448	Purchases returns	328
		Cash sales	568

(b)

Yes	
No	✔

7 The journal

7.1 Payroll transactions

7.2

Date 20-4	Details	Reference	Dr £	Cr £
1 Feb	Vehicle	GL	6,500	
	Fixtures and fittings	GL	2,800	
	Inventory	GL	4,100	
	Cash	CB	150	
	Bank	CB	1,250	
	Loan from uncle	GL		5,000
	Capital	GL		9,800
			14,800	14,800
	Assets and liabilities at the start of business			

7.3   **(a)**

Account name	Amount £	Debit	Credit
Irrecoverable debts	560	✔	
Value Added Tax	112	✔	
Sales ledger control	672		✔

(b)

Account name	Amount £	Debit	Credit
Sales ledger control	14,275	✔	
Purchases ledger control	7,392		✔
Inventory	4,107	✔	
Office equipment	10,400	✔	
Cash at bank	2,822	✔	
Rent and rates	4,086	✔	
Miscellaneous expenses	794	✔	
Wages	2,397	✔	
Loan from bank	6,250		✔
Capital	25,239		✔
Journal to record the opening entries of the new business			

7.4

(a)

Account name	Amount £	Debit	Credit
Wages expense	24,489	✔	
Wages control	24,489		✔

(b)

Account name	Amount £	Debit	Credit
Wages control	4,580	✔	
HM Revenue & Customs	4,580		✔

(c)

Account name	Amount £	Debit	Credit
Wages control	17,845	✔	
Bank	17,845		✔

(d)

Account name	Amount £	Debit	Credit
Wages control	2,064	✔	
Pension fund	2,064		✔

8 The trial balance and correction of errors

8.1 **(a)** Principle

(b) Commission

(c) Original entry

(d) Compensating

(e) Reversal of entries

(f) Omission

8.2

Debit		Credit	
Telephone expenses	£250	Bank	£250
Telephone expenses	£250	Bank	£250

8.3

(a)

Account name	Amount £	Debit	Credit
Suspense	2,825		✔

(b)

Error in the general ledger	Error disclosed by the trial balance	Error NOT disclosed by the trial balance
The cost of diesel fuel, £50, has been debited in the cash book and credited to vehicles account		✔
A credit sale of £225 has not been entered in the accounts		✔
The balance of wages account has been calculated incorrectly	✔	
A cash purchase of £85 has been recorded in the cash book only	✔	
The cost of stationery, £54, has been recorded as £45 in the cash book and stationery account		✔
Rent paid of £450 has been debited to rent paid account and debited in the cash book	✔	

8.4

(a)   **(1)**

Account name	Amount £	Debit	Credit
Purchases ledger control	2,120	✔	

(2)

Account name	Amount £	Debit	Credit
Purchases ledger control	2,544		✔

(3)

Account name	Amount £	Debit	Credit
Suspense	424	✔	

(b)   **(1)**

Account name	Amount £	Debit	Credit
Rent	525	✔	
Bank	525		✔

(2)

Account name	Amount £	Debit	Credit
Rent	525	✔	
Bank	525		✔

8.5

Office expenses Account

Details	Amount £	Details	Amount £
Office equipment	180		

Office equipment Account

Details	Amount £	Details	Amount £
		Office expenses	180

Sales returns Account

Details	Amount £	Details	Amount £
Suspense	295		

Suspense Account

Details	Amount £	Details	Amount £
Balance b/f	645	Sales returns	295
		Vehicle expenses	350

Vehicle expenses Account

Details	Amount £	Details	Amount £
Suspense	350		

8.6

Account name	Balances extracted on 30 June 20-9	Balances at 1 July 20-9	
	£	Debit £	Credit £
Inventory	8,692	8,692	
Sales ledger control	12,347	12,347	
Petty cash control	84	84	
Capital	15,287		15,287
Loan from bank	8,625		8,625
VAT owing to HM Revenue & Customs	2,733		2,733
Purchases ledger control	8,421		8,421
Bank (cash at bank)	1,596	1,596	
Sales	77,364		77,364
Sales returns	2,913	2,913	
Purchases	40,467	40,467	
Purchases returns	872		1,362
Wages	20,644	20,644	
Advertising	2,397	2,927	
Insurance	1,849	1,849	
Heating and lighting	1,066	1,066	
Rent and rates	3,862	3,862	
Vehicle expenses	2,035	1,945	
Vehicles	15,400	15,400	
Suspense account (credit balance)	50	–	–
Totals		113,792	113,792

for your notes

Practice assessment 1

Complete all 10 tasks.

Each task is independent. You will not need to refer to your answers in previous tasks.

The tasks are set in a business where the following apply:

- You are employed by the business, Murray Ltd, as a bookkeeper.

- Murray Ltd uses a manual bookkeeping system.

- Double-entry takes place in the general ledger. Individual accounts of trade receivables and trade payables are kept in the sales and purchases ledgers as subsidiary accounts.

- The cash book and petty cash book should be treated as part of the double-entry system unless the task instructions state otherwise.

- The VAT rate is 20%.

Task 1

Murray Ltd has started a new business, Murray Supplies, and a new set of accounts is to be opened. A partially completed journal to record the opening entries is shown below.

Record the journal entries needed in the accounts in the general ledger of Murray Supplies to deal with the opening entries.

Account name	Amount	Debit	Credit
	£	✔	✔
Cash	250		
Bank overdraft	2,359		
Vehicles	12,500		
Machinery	8,400		
Capital	25,410		
Inventory	3,987		
Sales ledger control	4,381		
Purchases ledger control	3,326		
Rent and rates	1,085		
Miscellaneous expenses	492		
Journal to record the opening entries of the new business			

Task 2

Murray Ltd pays its employees through the bank every month and maintains a wages control account. A summary of last month's payroll transactions is shown below.

Item	£
Gross wages	35,247
Income tax	4,780
Employer's National Insurance contributions	3,840
Employees' National Insurance contributions	2,860
Employer's pension contributions	1,740
Employees' pension contributions	1,740

Record the journal entries needed in the general ledger to:

(a)

Record the wages expense.

(b)

Record HM Revenue & Customs liability.

(c)

Record the net wages paid to the employees.

(d)

Record the pension fund liability.

Select your account names from the following list: Bank, Employees' National Insurance, Employer's National Insurance, HM Revenue & Customs, Income tax, Net wages, Pension fund, Wages control, Wages expense.

Enter the names and amounts and tick the appropriate debit or credit column.

(a)

Account name	Amount £	Debit ✔	Credit ✔

(b)

Account name	Amount £	Debit ✔	Credit ✔

(c)

Account name	Amount £	Debit ✔	Credit ✔

(d)

Account name	Amount £	Debit ✔	Credit ✔

Task 3

A credit customer, Froggatt Limited, has ceased trading, owing Murray Ltd £920 plus VAT at 20%.

(a)

Record the journal entries needed in the general ledger to write off the net amount and the VAT.

Select your account names from the following list: Murray Ltd, Froggatt Limited, Irrecoverable debts, Purchases, Purchases ledger control, Sales, Sales ledger control, Value Added Tax.

Account name	Amount £	Debit ✔	Credit ✔

(b)

Show which of the errors below are, or are not, disclosed by the trial balance.

Error in the general ledger	Error disclosed by the trial balance ✔	Error NOT disclosed by the trial balance ✔
Commission received of £150 has been credited to rent received account		
Sales returns of £225 have been credited to sales account		
A bank payment for vehicle repairs has been recorded in the cash book only		
The balance of sales account has been calculated incorrectly		

(c)

Classify the following errors:

	Error of omission ✔	Error of original entry ✔	Error of commission ✔
Discount received of £72 has been recorded in the discount received account as £27			
A bank payment to a credit supplier has not been entered in the cash book or the purchases ledger control account			
A sales invoice for £340 for Playwell Ltd has been debited to the account of Playtime Ltd			

Task 4

(a)

A direct debit for business rates of £609 has been entered in the accounts as £690.

Record the journal entries needed in the general ledger to remove the incorrect entry.

Select your account names from the following list: Bank, Cash, Direct debit, Purchases, Rates, Suspense.

Account name	Amount £	Debit ✔	Credit ✔

(b)

Record the journal entries needed in the general ledger to record the correct entry.

Select your account names from the following list: Bank, Cash, Direct debit, Purchases, Rates, Suspense.

Account name	Amount £	Debit ✔	Credit ✔

Task 5

Murray Ltd's initial trial balance includes a suspense account with a balance of £1,000.

The error has been traced to the purchases day book as shown below.

Purchases day book

Date 20-4	Details	Invoice number	Total £	VAT £	Net £
30 Jun	Maldanado and Co	5916	3,600	600	3,000
30 Jun	Murray Ltd	M/3421	1,680	280	1,400
30 Jun	Bromfield Supplies	B8624	480	80	400
	Totals		4,760	960	4,800

(a)

Identify the error and record the journal entries needed in the general ledger to:

    (1)   Remove the incorrect entry.

    (2)   Record the correct entry.

    (3)   Remove the suspense account balance.

Select your account name from the following list: Bromfield Supplies, Maldanado and Co, Murray Ltd, Purchases, Purchases day book, Purchases ledger control, Purchases returns, Purchases returns day book, Sales, Sales day book, Sales ledger control, Sales returns, Sales returns day book, Suspense, Value Added Tax.

(1)

Account name	Amount £	Debit ✔	Credit ✔

(2)

Account name	Amount £	Debit ✔	Credit ✔

(3)

Account name	Amount £	Debit ✔	Credit ✔

(b)

An entry to record a bank receipt of £220 for commission received has been reversed.

Record the journal entries needed in the general ledger to:

(1) Remove the incorrect entry.

(2) Record the correct entry.

Select your account names from the following list: Bank, Cash, Commission received, Purchases, Purchases ledger control, Sales, Sales ledger control, Suspense, Value Added Tax.

(1)

Account name	Amount £	Debit ✔	Credit ✔

(2)

Account name	Amount £	Debit ✔	Credit ✔

Task 6

Murray Ltd's trial balance included a suspense account. All the bookkeeping errors have now been traced and the journal entries shown below have been recorded.

Journal entries

Account name	Debit £	Credit £
Rent received	450	
Rent paid		450
Purchases	500	
Suspense		500
Office expenses	125	
Suspense		125

Post the journal entries to the general ledger accounts. Dates are not required.

Select your entries for the Details column from the following list: Balance b/f, Office expenses, Purchases, Rent paid, Rent received, Suspense.

Select your entries for the Amount column from: £450, £500, £125.

Rent received

Details	Amount £	Details	Amount £

Rent paid

Details	Amount £	Details	Amount £

Purchases

Details	Amount £	Details	Amount £

Suspense

Details	Amount £	Details	Amount £
Balance b/f	625		

Office expenses

Details	Amount £	Details	Amount £

Task 7

On 30 June Murray Ltd extracted an initial trial balance which did not balance, and a suspense account was opened. On 1 July journal entries were prepared to correct the errors that had been found, and to clear the suspense account. The list of balances in the initial trial balance, and the journal entries to correct the errors, are shown below.

Redraft the trial balance by placing the figures in the debit or credit column. You should take into account the journal entries (on next page) which will clear the suspense account.

Account name	Balances extracted on 30 June £	Balances at 1 July	
		Debit £	Credit £
Vehicles	17,800		
Inventory	4,925		
Sales ledger control	6,318		
Petty cash control	49		
Capital	18,835		
Loan from bank	3,841		
VAT owing to HM Revenue & Customs	1,596		
Purchases ledger control	4,389		
Bank overdraft	1,497		
Sales	86,833		
Sales returns	2,076		
Purchases	41,783		
Purchases returns	1,086		
Wages	33,965		
Advertising	3,864		
Insurance	1,597		
Heating and lighting	1,326		
Rent and rates	2,847		
Vehicle expenses	1,727		
Suspense account (credit balance)	200		
Totals			

Journal entries

Account name	Debit £	Credit £
Suspense	280	
Bank		280
Suspense	280	
Bank		280

Account name	Debit £	Credit £
Suspense	1,590	
Sales returns		1,590
Sales returns	1,950	
Suspense		1,950

Task 8

On 27 June Murray Ltd received the following bank statement as at 25 June.

Assume today's date is 30 June, unless told otherwise.

BANK STATEMENT				
Date 20-4	**Details**	**Paid out £**	**Paid in £**	**Balance £**
01 Jun	Balance brought forward			1,487 C
04 Jun	Cheque 114117	395		1,092 C
05 Jun	Cheque 114118	1,310		218 D
05 Jun	BACS credit: Cottle Ltd		4,806	4,588 C
18 Jun	Cheque 114119	2,218		2,370 C
20 Jun	Direct debit: Wyvern Council	235		2,135 C
21 Jun	BACS credit: Bayer Ltd		1,095	3,230 C
21 Jun	BACS credit: Allen plc		2,786	6,016 C
22 Jun	Direct debit: JA Finance	592		5,424 C
22 Jun	Cheque 114121	1,427		3,997 C
24 Jun	Paid into bank		2,108	6,105 C
24 Jun	Bank charges	45		6,060 C
D = Debit C = Credit				

The cash book as at 25 June is shown below.

CASH BOOK

Date 20-4	Details	Bank £	Date 20-4	Cheque number	Details	Bank £
01 Jun	Balance b/f	1,487	01 Jun	114117	Hendric & Co	395
04 Jun	Cottle Ltd	4,806	01 Jun	114118	Harrup & Noyes	1,310
20 Jun	W Waugh	2,108	10 Jun	114119	Farr Ltd	2,218
24 Jun	Pardo Ltd	1,746	18 Jun	114120	Bradnock Trading	1,036
24 Jun	Torre & Co	542	18 Jun	114121	Paxtons	1,427
			18 Jun	114122	Filiaps Ltd	798
			20 Jun		Wyvern Council	235

(a)

Check the items on the bank statement against the items in the cash book.

(b)

Enter any items in the cash book as needed.

(c)

Total the cash book and clearly show the balance carried down at 25 June (closing balance) and brought down at 26 June (opening balance).

Select your entries for the Details column from the following list: Allen plc, Balance b/d, Balance c/d, Bank charges, Bayer Ltd, Bradnock Trading, Closing balance, Cottle Ltd, Farr Ltd, Filiaps Ltd, Harrup & Noyes, Hendric & Co, JA Finance, Opening balance, Pardo Ltd, Paxtons, Torre & Co, W Waugh, Wyvern Council.

Task 9

On 1 October Murray Ltd received the following bank statement as at 30 September.

BANK STATEMENT					
Date **20-4**	**Details**	**Paid out** £	**Paid in** £	**Balance** £	
01 Sep	Balance b/f			−94	D
02 Sep	Credit 100535		2,863	2,769	C
07 Sep	145002	168		2,601	C
11 Sep	145003	780		1,821	C
12 Sep	Credit 100536		563	2,384	C
17 Sep	145004	129		2,255	C
19 Sep	BACS J Jones Ltd		472	2,727	C
22 Sep	dd Wyvern Council	609		2,118	C
24 Sep	Credit 100538		439	2,557	C
25 Sep	Bank charges	66		2,491	C

The cash book as at 30 September is shown below.

Date 20-4	Details	Amount £	Date 20-4	Cheque number	Details	Amount £
01-Sep	Balance b/f	2,769	05-Sep	145002	Farr Ltd	168
12-Sep	Torre & Co	563	08-Sep	145003	Paxtons	780
19-Sep	BACS J Jones	472	12-Sep	145004	Donfar & Co	129
24-Sep	LLR Ltd	439	16-Sep	145005	O Borne	760
29-Sep	W Waugh	946	22-Sep	DD	Wyvern CC	609
			23-Sep	BACS	Filiaps	1,055
			25-Sep		Bank charges	66

(a)

Identify the three transactions that are included in the cash book but missing from the bank statement and complete the bank reconciliation statement below as at 30 September.

Select your entries for the name boxes from the following list:
Bank charges, O Borne, Donfar & Co, Farr Ltd, Filiaps, J Jones, LLR Ltd, Paxtons, Torre & Co, W Waugh, Wyvern CC.

Bank reconciliation statement as at 30 September 20-4	
Balance as per bank statement	£
Add:	
Name:	£
Total to add	£
Less:	
Name:	£
Name:	£
Total to subtract	£
Balance as per cash book	£

(b)

Complete the following text below by choosing the correct words from the boxes below and entering them in the boxes in the text.

cash book	bank statement	ledger	error
discrepancy	fraud	regular	daily
timing	date	independent	similarity

It is important to reconcile the cash book to the [　　　　　　　　　　　]

on a [　　　　　　　　　　　] basis.

The bank statement provides an [　　　　　　　　　　　] accounting

record and helps to prevent [　　　　　　　　　　　].

It also highlights any [　　　　　　　　　　　] differences and explains

why there is a [　　　　　　　　　　　] between the bank statement

balance and the [　　　　　　　　　　　] balance.

Task 10

This is a summary of transactions with credit suppliers during the month of June.

(a)

Show whether each entry will be a debit or a credit in the purchases ledger control account in the general ledger.

Details	Amount	Debit	Credit
	£	✔	✔
Balance of credit suppliers at 1 June	18,392		
Goods bought on credit	6,874		
Payments made to credit suppliers	8,937		
Discounts received	154		
Goods returned to credit suppliers	529		

(b)

What will be the balance brought down on 1 July on the above account?

	✔
Dr £17,012	
Cr £17,012	
Dr £15,646	
Cr £15,646	
Dr £21,138	
Cr £21,138	

The following credit balances were in the purchases ledger on 1 July.

	£
Hamilton Ltd	3,486
Gusson & Co	1,089
Palgrave Supplies	2,627
Ikpusu & Co	4,321
Lorenz Ltd	747
McDiarmid plc	3,961

(c)

Reconcile the balances shown above with the purchases ledger control account balance calculated in part (b).

	£
Balance on purchases ledger control account at 30 June	
Total of the purchases ledger balances at 30 June	
Difference	

(d)

What may have caused the difference you calculated in part (c)?

	✔
An invoice was entered twice in the purchases ledger	
A credit note was entered twice in the purchases ledger	
A credit note was not entered in the purchases ledger control account	
Settlement discount was not entered in the purchases ledger control account	

(e)

Tick **TWO** of the following statements that are true.

	✔
Reconciliation of the purchases ledger control account assures managers that the amount showing as outstanding to suppliers is correct	
The balance of the purchases ledger control account should agree to the total of the balances in the sales ledger	
The balance of the sales ledger control account should agree to the total of the aged trade payables analysis	
Reconciliation of the purchases ledger control account highlights any differences between the subsidiary ledger total and the control account balance	

Task 11

The following is a list of the VAT totals from Murray Ltd's books of prime entry:

Books of prime entry	VAT totals for quarter £
Sales day book	14,800
Purchases day book	9,080
Sales returns day book	368
Purchases returns day book	248
Cash book: cash sales	376

Other VAT items for the quarter are as follows:

VAT on petty cash payments	17
VAT on irrecoverable debt written off	108
VAT on purchase of computer equipment	575
VAT paid to HMRC	9,804

(a)

What will be the entries in the VAT control account to record the VAT transactions in the quarter?

Select your entries for the Details column from the following list: Bank, Cash sales, Computer equipment, Irrecoverable debts, Petty cash, Purchases, Purchases day book, Purchases returns, Purchases returns day book, Sales, Sales day book, Sales returns, Sales returns day book, Value Added Tax.

VAT control account

Details	Amount £	Details	Amount £
		Balance b/f	9,804

(b)

The VAT Return has been completed and shows an amount owing to HM Revenue & Customs of £5,276.

Is the VAT Return correct?

	✔
Yes	
No	

(c)

Show whether the following statements are true or false.

	True ✔	False ✔
The VAT control account is used to calculate how much VAT is due to, or sometimes from, HMRC		
A debit balance on the VAT control account indicates that the business is due a refund from HMRC		
A bank payment of VAT due to HMRC will be entered as a debit in the VAT control account		

Task 12

(a)

Show the most appropriate form of payment for each transaction below by joining with a line each box on the left with the appropriate one on the right.

Payment to a credit supplier of £1,079	CHAPS
Payment for milk and biscuits for staff refreshments	Standing order
Payment of £90,000 for property purchase	Cash
Variable quarterly payment for telephone services	Credit card
Monthly payment of rent (same amount each month)	Direct debit
Payment for an online purchase of shop fitting	Faster payments

(b)

Show whether the following statements are true or false.

	True ✔	False ✔
Building societies offer banking services predominantly to individuals whereas banks offer banking services to both individuals and businesses		
A bank draft is signed by a business customer to authorise a direct debit payment		
If the business has an overdraft, the bank owes the business money		

(c)

Complete the text below by choosing the correct words from the following options:

variable	shredded	returned to the bank	retention

fixed by the bank	formatting

A business should have a banking document [ ] policy.

The length of time records should be kept is [ ] according to the type of record.

After this period of time the document should be [ ] .

Practice
assessment 2

Complete all 12 tasks.

Each task is independent. You will not need to refer to your answers in previous tasks.

The tasks are set in a business where the following apply:

- You are employed by the business, Cucina Ltd, as a bookkeeper.

- Cucina Ltd uses a manual bookkeeping system.

- Double-entry takes place in the general ledger. Individual accounts of trade receivables and trade payables are kept in the sales and purchases ledgers as subsidiary accounts.

- The cash book and petty cash book should be treated as part of the double-entry system unless the task instructions state otherwise.

- The VAT rate is 20%.

Task 1

Cucina Ltd has started a new business, Cucina Capers, and a new set of accounts are to be opened. A partially completed journal to record the opening entries is shown below.

Record the journal entries needed in the accounts in the general ledger of Cucina Capers to deal with the opening entries.

Account name	Amount £	Debit ✔	Credit ✔
Cash	150		
Cash at bank	12,350		
Capital	23,456		
Fixtures and fittings	2,100		
Insurance	825		
Loan from bank	10,000		
Miscellaneous expenses	218		
Motor vehicle	15,650		
Office expenses	613		
Rent and rates	1,550		
Journal to record the opening entries of new business			

Task 2

Cucina Ltd pays its employees by cheque every month and maintains a wages control account. A summary of last month's payroll transactions is shown below:

Item	£
Gross wages	6,236
Employer's NI	730
Employees' NI	620
Income tax	1,808
Trade Union fees	300

Record the journal entries needed in the general ledger to:

(a)

Record the wages expense.

(b)

Record the HM Revenue & Customs liability.

(c)

Record the net wages paid to the employees.

(d)

Record the Trade Union liability.

Select your account names from the following list: Bank, Employees' NI, Employer's NI, HM Revenue & Customs, Income tax, Net wages, Trade Union, Wages control, Wages expense.

Enter the names and amounts and tick the appropriate debit or credit column.

(a)

Account name	Amount £	Debit ✔	Credit ✔

(b)

Account name	Amount £	Debit ✔	Credit ✔

(c)

Account name	Amount £	Debit ✔	Credit ✔

(d)

Account name	Amount £	Debit ✔	Credit ✔

Task 3

A credit customer, B B Brand Ltd, has ceased trading, owing Cucina Ltd £1,560 plus VAT at 20%.

(a)

Record the journal entries needed in the general ledger to write off the net amount and the VAT.

Select your account names from the following list: B B Brand Ltd, Irrecoverable debts, Cucina Ltd, Purchases, Purchases ledger control, Sales, Sales ledger control, VAT.

Enter the names and amounts and tick the appropriate debit or credit column.

Account name	Amount £	Debit ✔	Credit ✔

(b)

Show which of the errors below are, or are not, disclosed by the trial balance.

Error in the general ledger	Error disclosed by the trial balance ✔	Error NOT disclosed by the trial balance ✔
Recording a bank payment for heat and light on the debit side of both the bank and heat and light account		
Incorrectly calculating the balance on the rent account		
Recording a payment by cheque to a creditor in the bank account and purchases ledger only		
Recording a bank payment of £470 for motor repairs as £4700 in both accounts		

(c)

Classify the following errors:

	Reversal of entries ✔	Error of original entry ✔	Error of principle ✔
Recording a payment for motor repairs in the motor vehicles account			
Recording a sales credit note on the debit side of the sales ledger control account and the credit side of the sales returns account			
Recording a bank payment for a telephone bill as £249 in both accounts when the actual bill was for £294			

Task 4

(a)

A standing order for rent paid of £1,250 has been entered in the accounts as £1,520.

Record the journal entries needed in the general ledger to remove the incorrect entry.

Select your account names from the following list: Bank, Cash, Standing order, Purchases, Rent paid, Rent received, Suspense.

Enter the names and amounts and tick the appropriate debit or credit column.

Account name	Amount £	Debit ✔	Credit ✔

(b)

Record the journal entries needed in the general ledger to record the correct entry.

Select your account names from the following list: Bank, Cash, Standing order, Purchases, Rent paid, Rent received, Suspense.

Enter the names and amounts and tick the appropriate debit or credit column.

Account name	Amount £	Debit ✔	Credit ✔

Task 5

Cucina Ltd's initial trial balance includes a suspense account with a balance of £100.

The error has been traced to the sales returns day book shown below.

Sales returns day book

Date 20-4	Details	Credit note number	Total £	VAT £	Net £
30 Jun	Barber Bates Ltd	367	720	120	600
30 Jun	GTK Ltd	368	4,320	720	3,600
30 Jun	Peer Prints	369	960	160	800
	Totals		6,000	1,100	5,000

(a)

Identify the error and record the journal entries needed in the general ledger to:
  (1) Remove the incorrect entry.
  (2) Record the correct entry.
  (3) Remove the suspense account balance.

Select your account names from the following list: Barber Bates Ltd, GTK Ltd, Peer Prints, Purchases, Purchases day book, Purchases ledger control, Purchases returns, Purchases returns day book, Sales, Sales day book, Sales ledger control, Sales returns, Sales returns day book, Suspense, VAT.

Enter the names and amounts and tick the appropriate debit or credit column.

(1)

Account name	Amount £	Debit ✔	Credit ✔

(2)

Account name	Amount £	Debit ✔	Credit ✔

(3)

Account name	Amount £	Debit ✔	Credit ✔

(b)

An entry to record a bank payment of £350 for heat and light has been reversed.

Record the journal entries needed in the general ledger to:

    (1)   Remove the incorrect entry.

    (2)   Record the correct entry.

Select your account names from the following list: Bank, Cash, Heat and light, Purchases, Purchases ledger control, Sales, Sales ledger control, Suspense, VAT.

Enter the names and amounts and tick the appropriate debit or credit column.

(1)

Account name	Amount £	Debit ✔	Credit ✔

(2)

Account name	Amount £	Debit ✔	Credit ✔

Task 6

Cucina Ltd's trial balance included a suspense account. All the bookkeeping errors have now been traced and the journal entries shown below have been recorded.

Journal entries

Account name	Debit £	Credit £
Office stationery	167	
Suspense		167
Suspense	1,800	
Rent and rates		1,800
Bank interest received	98	
Bank interest charged		98

Post the journal entries to the general ledger accounts. Dates are not required.

Select your entries for the Details column from the following list: Balance b/f, Bank interest charged, Bank interest received, Office stationery, Rent and rates, Suspense.

Enter the names and amounts and tick the appropriate debit or credit column.

Office stationery Account

Details	Amount £	Details	Amount £

Rent and rates Account

Details	Amount £	Details	Amount £

Suspense Account

Details	Amount £	Details	Amount £
		Balance b/f	1,633

Bank interest received Account

Details	Amount £	Details	Amount £

Bank interest charged Account

Details	Amount £	Details	Amount £

Task 7

On 30 June, Cucina Ltd extracted an initial trial balance which did not balance, and a suspense account was opened. On 1 July journal entries were prepared to correct the errors that had been found, and clear the suspense account. The list of balances in the initial trial balance, and the journal entries to correct the errors, are shown below.

Redraft the trial balance by placing the figures in the debit or credit column. You should take into account the journal entries on the next page which will clear the suspense account.

	Balances extracted on 30 June	Balances at 1 July	
	£	Debit £	Credit £
Motor vehicles	34,536		
Fixtures and fittings	17,350		
Inventory	7,300		
Bank overdraft	5,521		
Petty cash	100		
Sales ledger control	100,625		
Purchases ledger control	56,119		
VAT owing to HM Revenue & Customs	8,300		
Capital	22,844		
Sales	222,955		
Purchases	112,250		
Purchases returns	6,780		
Wages	25,700		
Motor expenses	1,368		
Office expenses	3,354		
Rent and rates	1,444		
Heat and light	2,155		
Insurance	3,165		
Miscellaneous expenses	2,220		
Suspense account (debit balance)	10,952		
Totals			

Journal entries

Account name	Debit £	Credit £
Bank	5,521	
Suspense		5,521
Bank	5,521	
Suspense		5,521

Account name	Debit £	Credit £
Purchases returns	6,780	
Suspense		6,780
Purchases returns		6,870
Suspense	6,870	

Task 8

On 28 June Cucina Ltd received the following bank statement as at 23 June.

Assume today's date is 30 June, unless told otherwise.

Midway Bank PLC, 52 The Parade, Darton, DF10 9SW				
To: Cucina Ltd Account No 39103988 23 June 20-4				
Statement of Account				
Date	Detail	Paid out	Paid in	Balance
20-4		£	£	£
04 June	Balance b/f			15,189 C
04 June	Cheque 111042	10,000		5,189 C
04 June	Cheque 111043	1,420		3,769 C
05 June	Cheque 111044	80		3,689 C
06 June	Cheque 111047	2,500		1,189 C
12 June	Bank Giro Credit Cabot and Co		571	1,760 C
13 June	Cheque 111045	795		965 C
13 June	Direct Debit LMBC	150		815 C
20 June	Direct Debit Insurance Direct	850		35 D
23 June	Bank Charges	88		123 D
23 June	Overdraft fee	30		153 D
23 June	Paid in at Midway Bank		175	22 C
D = Debit C = Credit				

Cash book as at 23 June

Date 20-4	Details	Bank £	Date 20-4	Cheque number	Details	Bank £
01 June	Balance b/f	15,189	01 June	111042	Prime kitchens	10,000
16 June	Britten & Bond	175	01 June	111043	Equipdirect	1,420
20 June	Macklin Ltd	950	01 June	111044	Long and Lane	80
21 June	Randle fitments	300	01 June	111045	BLH Ltd	795
			02 June	111046	MVR Ltd	652
			02 June	111047	Fairfield Ltd	2,500
			13 June	111048	Makin and King	450
			13 June		LBMC	150

(a)

Check the items on the bank statement against the items in the cash book.

(b)

Enter any items in the cash book as needed.

(c)

Total the cash book and clearly show the balance carried down at 23 June (closing balance) and brought down at 24 June (opening balance).

Select your entries for the Details column from the following list: Balance b/d, Balance c/d, Bank charges, BLH Ltd, Britten & Bond, Cabot and Co, Closing balance, Equipdirect, Fairfield Ltd, Insurance Direct, LBMC, Long and Lane, Macklin Ltd, Makin and King, MVR Ltd, Opening balance, Overdraft fees, Prime Kitchens, Randle Fitments.

Task 9

On 1 October Cucina Ltd received the following bank statement as at 30 September.

BANK STATEMENT				
Date 20-4		**Paid out** £	**Paid in** £	**Balance** £
01 Sep	Balance b/f			252 C
02 Sep	112001	1,628		−1,376 D
04 Sep	Paid in		2,307	931 C
08 Sep	112003	186		745 C
12 Sep	112002	870		−125 D
13 Sep	Paid in		653	528 C
18 Sep	112004	219		309 C
20 Sep	BACS Cabot and Co		742	1,051 C
23 Sep	SO Commercial Prop	600		451 C
25 Sep	Paid in		349	800 C
26 Sep	Bank charges	48		752 C

The cash book as at 30 September is shown below.

Date 20-4	Details	Amount £	Date 20-4	Cheque number	Details	Amount £
04 Sep	Brownlow	2,307	01 Sep		Balance b/f	1,376
13 Sep	Peer Prints	653	06 Sep	112003	Ace Timber	186
20 Sep	BACS Cabot and Co	742	09 Sep	112002	Fairfield Ltd	870
25 Sep	GTK Ltd	349	13 Sep	112004	BLH Ltd	219
30 Sep	Barber Bates Ltd	469	17 Sep	112005	Bridge Tools	607
			23 Sep	SO	Commercial Prop	600
			24 Sep	BACS	Tenon Ltd	1,505
			26 Sep		Bank charges	48

(a)

Identify the three transactions that are included in the cash book but missing from the bank statement and complete the bank reconciliation statement below as at 30 September.

Select your entries for the name rows from the following list: Ace Timber, Bank charges, Barber Bates Ltd, BLH Ltd, Bridge Tools, Brownlow, Cabot and Co, Commercial Prop, Fairfield Ltd, GTK Ltd, Peer Prints, Tenon Ltd.

Bank reconciliation statement as at 30 September 20-4	
Balance as per bank statement	£
Add:	
Name:	£
Total to add	£
Less:	
Name:	£
Name:	£
Total to subtract	£
Balance as per cash book	£

(b)

Link each item in the boxes on the left with the appropriate definition on the right by drawing a line between the two boxes.

Unpresented cheque	An amount paid into the bank but not yet showing on the bank statement
Outstanding lodgement	A document used to explain why there may be a difference between the cash book balance and the bank statement balance
Bank reconciliation statement	Discrepancy arising from a delay in the recording of payments and receipts on the bank's records
Timing difference	An amount recorded as a payment in the cash book but not yet appearing on the bank statement

Task 10

(a)

This is a summary of transactions with suppliers during the month of June.

Show whether each entry will be a debit or credit in the Purchases ledger control account in the Main ledger.

Details	Amount £	Debit ✔	Credit ✔
Balance of creditors at 1 June	50,530		
Goods bought on credit	17,504		
Payments made to credit suppliers	20,672		
Discount received	392		
Goods returned to credit suppliers	784		

(b)

What will be the balance brought down on 1 July on the above account?

	✔
Dr £54,874	
Cr £54,874	
Dr £46,970	
Cr £46,970	
Dr £46,186	
Cr £46,186	

(c)

The following credit balances were in the subsidiary (purchases) ledger on 1 July.

	£
MMM Ltd	21,300
Walton Doors Ltd	4,198
Bramble and Barnet	123
Croxford and Company	15,530
Goodman Timber	1,119
Masefield Limited	3,524

Reconcile the balances shown above with the purchases ledger control account balance you have calculated in part (a).

	£
Purchases ledger control account balance as at 30 June	
Total of subsidiary (purchases) ledger accounts as at 30 June	
Difference	

(d)

What may have caused the difference you calculated in part (b)?   ✔

Goods returned may have been omitted from the subsidiary ledger	
Discounts received may have been omitted from the subsidiary ledger	
Goods returned may have been entered in the subsidiary ledger twice	
Discounts received may have been entered in the subsidiary ledger twice	

(e)

Show whether the following statements are true or false.

	True ✔	False ✔
Reconciliation of the sales ledger control account assures managers that the amount showing as outstanding from customers is correct		
The balance of the sales ledger control account should agree to the total of the balances in the sales ledger		
The balance of the sales ledger control account should agree to the total of the aged trade payables analysis		
Reconciliation of the sales ledger control account highlights any differences between the subsidiary ledger total and the control account balance		

Task 11

The following is a list of the VAT totals from Cucina Ltd's books of prime entry:

Books of prime entry	**VAT totals for quarter**
	£
Sales day book	34,400
Purchases day book	19,600
Sales returns day book	560
Purchases returns day book	1,520
Cash book: cash sales	64

Other VAT items for the quarter are as follows:

VAT on petty cash payments	11
VAT on irrecoverable debt written off	96
VAT on purchase of computer equipment	420
VAT paid to HMRC	4,666

(a)

What will be the entries in the VAT control account to record the VAT transactions in the quarter?

Select your entries for the Details columns from the following list: Bank, Cash book, Irrecoverable debts, Office equipment, Petty cash, Purchases, Purchases day book, Purchases returns, Purchases returns day book, Cash sales, Sales day book, Sales returns, Sales returns day book, VAT.

VAT control Account

Details	Amount £	Details	Amount £
		Balance b/f	4,666

(b)

The VAT Return has been completed and shows an amount owing from HM Revenue & Customs of £15,393.

Is the VAT Return correct?

	✔
Yes	
No	

(c)

Show whether the following statements are true or false.

	True ✔	False ✔
VAT totals from the day books are posted to the VAT control account		
A credit balance on the VAT control account indicates that the business owes money to HMRC		
A refund of VAT from HMRC will be entered as a debit in the VAT control account		

Task 12

Cucina Ltd receives payment from customers and makes payments to suppliers in a variety of ways.

(a)

Select **TWO** checks that have to be made on each of the two payment methods shown below when received from customers.

Checks to be made	Cheque ✔	Telephone credit card payment ✔
Check expiry date		
Check issue number		
Check not post-dated		
Check security number		
Check words and figures match		
Check card has not been tampered with		

(b)

Show whether each of the statements below is true or false.

	True ✔	False ✔
When Cucina Ltd makes payments to suppliers by credit card, the amount leaves the bank current account immediately		
When Cucina Ltd makes payments to suppliers by debit card, the amount paid does not affect the bank current account		

(c)

Which **TWO** of the documents below are banking documents that must be retained by Cucina Ltd?

	✔
Aged trade receivable analysis	
Aged trade payable analysis	
Bank statements	
Credit cards	
Debit cards	
Paying in slip stubs	
Remittance advice notes	
Supplier invoices	

Practice assessment 3

Complete all 12 tasks.

Each task is independent. You will not need to refer to your answers in previous tasks.

The tasks are set in a business where the following apply:

- You are employed by the business, Quaver Music, as a bookkeeper.

- Quaver Music uses a manual bookkeeping system.

- Double-entry takes place in the general ledger. Individual accounts of trade receivables and trade payables are kept in the sales and purchases ledgers as subsidiary accounts.

- The cash book and petty cash book should be treated as part of the double-entry system unless the task instructions state otherwise.

- The VAT rate is 20%.

Task 1

Quaver Music started a new business called Quaver Promotions and a new set of accounts is to be opened. A partially completed journal to record the opening entries is shown below.

Complete the journal by showing whether each amount would be in the debit or credit column.

Account name	Amount	Debit	Credit
	£	✔	✔
Capital	5,000		
Bank loan	6,000		
Computer equipment	2,622		
Inventory	3,178		
Trade payables	3,814		
Bank (debit balance)	5,984		
Cash	239		
Discounts received	32		
Premises expenses	2,187		
VAT (debit balance)	636		

Task 2

Quaver Music pays its employees by bank transfer every month and maintains a wages control account. A summary of last month's payroll transactions is shown below:

Payroll transactions	£
Gross wages	46,450
Income tax	4,798
Employees' NI	2,467
Employer's NI	2,694
Employees' pension contributions	2,321
Employer's pension contributions	1,032

(a)

Show the journal entries needed in the general ledger to record the wages expense.

Select your account names from the following list: Bank, Employees' NI, Employer's NI, HM Revenue & Customs, Income tax, Net wages, Pension, Wages control, Wages expense.

Enter the names and amounts and tick the appropriate debit or credit column.

Account name	Amount £	Debit ✔	Credit ✔

(b)

Show the journal entries needed in the general ledger to record the net wages paid to employees.

Select your account names from the following list: Bank, Employees' NI, Employer's NI, HM Revenue & Customs, Income tax, Net wages, Pension, Wages control, Wages expense.

Enter the names and amounts and tick the appropriate debit or credit column.

Account name	Amount £	Debit ✔	Credit ✔

Task 3

(a)

Show by ticking in the appropriate column which of the errors below are, or are not, disclosed by the trial balance.

Errors	Error disclosed by the trial balance ✔	Error NOT disclosed by the trial balance ✔
A cash purchase has been entered in the cash book but not in the purchases account		
Discount allowed of £98 has been recorded in the discount allowed account as £89		
A receipt from a credit customer has not been entered in the cash book or the sales ledger control account		
A purchase credit note for £296 has been debited to the purchases account and credited to the purchases ledger control account		

(b)

Classify the following errors by ticking in the appropriate column.

	Error of principle ✔	Compensating error ✔	Error of commission ✔
The purchase of studio recording equipment for £3,000 has been debited to the recording expense account			
The sales account has been overcast by £10. The purchases account has also been overcast by £10			
A purchase invoice for £235 for Stage Supplies Ltd has been credited to the account of Stage Equipment Ltd			

(c)

A credit customer, MJ Studios, has ceased trading owing Quaver Music £132 including VAT.

Record the journal entries needed in the general ledger to write off the net amount and the VAT.

Select your account names from the following list: MJ Studios, Irrecoverable debts, Purchases, Purchases ledger control, Quaver Music, Sales, Sales ledger control, VAT.

Enter the names and amounts and tick the appropriate debit or credit column.

Account name	Amount £	Debit ✔	Credit ✔

Task 4

(a)

A cheque payment for £3,421 for new recording equipment has been entered in the accounts as £4,321.

Record the journal entries needed in the general ledger to remove the incorrect entry.

Select your account names from the following list: Bank, Cash, Purchases, Recording equipment, Sales, Suspense.

Enter the names and amounts and tick the appropriate debit or credit column.

Account name	Amount £	Debit ✔	Credit ✔

(b)

Record the journal entries needed in the general ledger to record the correct entry.

Select your account names from the following list: Bank, Cash, Purchases, Recording equipment, Sales, Suspense.

Enter the names and amounts and tick the appropriate debit or credit column.

Account name	Amount £	Debit ✔	Credit ✔

Task 5

Quaver Music's trial balance failed to balance. The debit column totalled £156,966 and the credit column £156,774.

(a)

What entry would be needed in the suspense account to balance the trial balance?

Account name	Amount £	Debit ✔	Credit ✔
Suspense			

The error has now been identified as VAT that should have been posted to the VAT account from the debit side of the cash book as shown below:

Cash book – debit side

Date 20-4	Details	Discount allowed	VAT £	Bank £
30 June	Balance b/f			6,883
30 June	Parton & Co	10		545
30 June	Cash sales		88	440
30 June	Winehouse Ltd			640
30 June	Cash sales		104	520
	Totals	10	192	9,028

(b)

Record the journal entry needed in the general ledger to record the correct entry that should have been made from the cash book.

Account name	Amount £	Debit ✔	Credit ✔

(c)

Record the journal entry needed in the general ledger to remove the suspense account balance arising from the error.

Account name	Amount £	Debit ✔	Credit ✔

(d)

Show which **FOUR** of the following transactions would be entered in the journal.

	✔
Bank loan repayment	
Irrecoverable debt write off	
Opening entries at start of business	
Payment of VAT owing to HMRC	
Payroll transactions	
Purchase of non-current assets	
Transfer of cash from cash sales to bank	

Task 6

Quaver Music's trial balance included a suspense account. All of the errors have now been traced and the journal entries are shown below.

Account name	Debit	Credit
Sales	99	
Suspense		99
Suspense	1,612	
VAT		1,612
Bank interest paid	52	
Bank charges		52

Post the journal entries to the general ledger accounts below. Dates are not required.

Select your entries for the Details column from: Bank charges, Bank interest paid, Sales, Suspense.

Select your entries for the Amounts column from: £99, £1,612, £52.

Sales Account

Details	Amount £	Details	Amount £

VAT Account

Details	Amount £	Details	Amount £

Bank interest paid Account

Details	Amount £	Details	Amount £

Bank charges Account

Details	Amount £	Details	Amount £

Suspense Account

Details	Amount £	Details	Amount £
		Balance b/f	1,513

Task 7

On 30 June Quaver Music extracted an initial trial balance which did not balance and the suspense account was opened with a debit balance of £590. The errors were found and on 1 July journal entries were prepared to correct them and clear the suspense account. The journal entries and the initial trial balance are shown below.

Redraft the initial trial balance by placing the figures in the debit or credit column. You should take into account the journal entries which will clear the suspense account.

Journal entries

Account name	Debit	Credit
Bank	537	
Suspense		537

Account name	Debit	Credit
Discounts allowed	53	
Suspense		53

Account name	Amount £	Debit ✔	Credit ✔
Capital	25,672		
Bank loan	12,000		
Computer equipment	10,024		
Recording equipment	5,412		
Inventory	2,555		
Purchases ledger control	2,299		
Bank overdraft	1,736		
Cash	250		
Discounts allowed	244		
Discounts received	105		
Premises expenses	2,187		
VAT owing to HMRC	3,647		
Sales	62,988		
Purchases	35,212		
Sales ledger control	7,298		
Administration expenses	3,611		
Wages	41,064		
Suspense	590		

Task 8

On 1 August Quaver Music received the following bank statement as at 31 July.

BANK STATEMENT					
Date 20-4	Details	Paid out £	Paid in £	Balance £	
01-Jul	Balance b/f			1,180	D
02-Jul	100150	556		1,736	D
03-Jul	100151	862		2,598	D
04-Jul	Paid in		3170	572	C
08-Jul	100153	168		404	C
10-Jul	SO National Tel	110		294	C
12-Jul	100152	785		491	D
13-Jul	Paid in		2563	2,072	C
18-Jul	100154	129		1,943	C
20-Jul	BACS Ciccone		2047	3,990	C
23-Jul	DD EDS Electricity	520		3,470	C
24-Jul	Transfer: A Adkins	1005		2,465	C
25-Jul	Paid in		2943	5,408	C
28-Jul	Credit charges	62		5,346	C
31-Jul	Multiple beneficiary	5236		110	C

(a)

Check the items on the bank statement against the items in the cash book.

(b)

Enter any items into the cash book as needed.

(c)

Total the cash book and clearly show the balance carried down at 31 July and brought down at 1 August.

Select your entries in the Details column from the following list: A Adkins, Arma Trading, Balance b/f, Balance c/f, K Bush, Credit charges, Carpenter Ltd, Ciccone, Electricity, Hynde Music, C King, A Murray, Telephone, Wages.

Date 20-4	Details	Amount £	Date 20-4	Cheque number	Details	Amount £
04 Jul	Carpenter Ltd	3,170	01 Jul		Balance b/f	1,736
13 Jul	C King	2,563	01 Jul	100151	Arma Trading	862
25 Jul	A Murray	2,943	06 Jul	100153	K Bush	168
			07 Jul	100152	Hynde Music	785
			10 Jul	SO	Telephone	110
			13 Jul	100154	Lennox & Co	129
			24 Jul	BACS	A Adkins	1,005
			31 Jul	BACS	Wages	5,236

Task 9

On 1 October Quaver Music received the following bank statement as at 30 September.

BANK STATEMENT				
Date 20-4	Details	Paid out £	Paid in £	Balance £
01-Sep	Balance b/f			7,635 C
04-Sep	100185	1,655		5,980 C
07-Sep	Paid in		1,992	7,972 C
09-Sep	100186	159		7,813 C
10-Sep	SO National Tel	110		7,703 C
19-Sep	100187	1,029		6,674 C
24-Sep	DD EDS	520		6,154 C
24-Sep	Transfer: MacColl Ltd	1,510		4,644 C
26-Sep	Paid in		2,464	7,108 C
30-Sep	Multiple beneficiary	6,143		965 C

The cash book as at 30 September is shown below.

Date 20-4	Details	Amount £	Date 20-4	Cheque number	Details	Amount £
01 Sep	Balance b/f	7,635	01 Sep	100185	Tunstall plc	1,655
07 Sep	J Stone	1,992	06 Sep	100186	K Bush	159
26 Sep	A Murray	2,464	10 Sep	BACS	Telephone	110
30 Sep	Winehouse Ltd	411	13 Sep	100187	Lennox & Co	1,029
30 Sep	Twain Trading	676	20 Sep	100188	E Harris	600
			24 Sep	DD	Electricity	520
			24 Sep	BACS	MacColl Ltd	1,510
			28 Sep	100189	N Simone	342
			30 Sep	BACS	Wages	6,143

(a)

Identify the four transactions that are included in the cash book but missing from the bank statement and complete the bank reconciliation statement below as at 30 September.

Select your entries for the name rows from the following list: K Bush, Electricity, E Harris, Lennox & Co, A MacColl Ltd, Murray, N Simone, J Stone, Telephone, Tunstall plc, Twain Trading, Wages, Winehouse Ltd.

Bank reconciliation statement as at 30 September 20-4	
Balance as per bank statement	£
Add:	
Name:	£
Name:	£
Total to add	£
Less:	
Name:	£
Name:	£
Total to subtract	£
Balance as per cash book	£

(b)

Complete the following text by choosing the correct words from the boxes below and entering them in the boxes in the text.

cash book	timing differences	bank	errors

security	reconciliation	authorised

The bank [   ] explains any difference between the

balance in the [   ] and the balance at the

[   ] .

It highlights any [   ] and [   ] .

Access to bank records should be restricted to [   ]

employees to safeguard the [   ] of payments and receipts.

Task 10

(a)

The following is a summary of transactions with credit customers during the month of July.

Show by ticking the appropriate column whether each entry will be a debit or credit in the sales ledger control account in the general ledger.

Sales ledger control account

Details	Amount £	Debit ✔	Credit ✔
Balance owing from credit customers at 1 July	7,298		
Money received from credit customers	6,450		
Discounts allowed	75		
Goods sold to credit customers	14,774		
Goods returned by credit customers	501		
Journal credit to correct an error	89		

(b)

The following is a summary of transactions with credit suppliers during the month of July.

Show by ticking the appropriate column whether each entry will be a debit or credit in the purchases ledger control account in the general ledger.

Purchases ledger control account

Details	Amount £	Debit ✔	Credit ✔
Balance owing to credit suppliers at 1 July	2,299		
Money paid to credit suppliers	2,276		
Discounts received	23		
Goods purchased from credit suppliers	5,113		
Goods returned to credit suppliers	108		

At the beginning of September the following balances were in the sales ledger:

Credit customers	Balances	
	Amount £	Debit/credit
J Stone	1,992	Debit
A Murray	2,464	Debit
Parton & Co	320	Credit
Winehouse Ltd	411	Debit
Carpenter Ltd	2,569	Debit
C King	1,945	Debit

(c)

What should the balance of the sales ledger control account be on 1 September in order for it to reconcile with the total of the balances in the sales ledger?

Balance	✔
Debit balance of £9,701	
Credit balance of £9,701	
Debit balance of £9,061	
Credit balance of £9,061	

(d)

Show whether the following statements are true or false.

	True ✔	False ✔
If an irrecoverable debt is not written off in the sales ledger control account, the balance on the account will be lower than it should be		
The balance of the purchases ledger control account should agree to the total of the aged trade payables analysis		
Reconciliation of the sales ledger control account highlights any differences between the subsidiary ledger total and the control account balance		

Task 11

The following is a record of the VAT values in Quaver Music's books of prime entry.

	£
VAT from Sales day book	17,200
VAT from Sales returns day book	280
VAT from Purchases day book	9,800
VAT from Purchases returns day book	760
VAT from Cash book (VAT on cash sales)	192
VAT on petty cash payments	9
VAT on irrecoverable debt written off	82
VAT on purchase of studio equipment	400
VAT paid to HMRC	6536

(a)

What will be the entries in the VAT control account to record the VAT transactions in the quarter?

Select your entries for the Details columns from the following list: Bank, Cash book, Irrecoverable debts, Petty cash, Purchases, Purchases returns, Sales, Sales returns, Studio equipment, VAT, and the VAT values from the table above.

VAT control account

Details	Amount £	Details	Amount £
		Balance b/f	6,536

The VAT Return has been completed and shows an amount owing to HMRC of £7,581.

(b)

Is the VAT Return correct?

	✔
Yes	
No	

(c)

Show whether the following statements are true or false.

	True ✔	False ✔
VAT on purchases and expenses can only be entered in the VAT account if the purchase document bears the VAT registration number of the supplier		
A bank receipt of a refund of VAT from HMRC would be shown as a credit in the VAT control account		
A bank payment of VAT due to HMRC will be entered as a credit in the VAT control account		

Task 12

(a)

The 2-4-6 cheque clearance cycle states that after a cheque has been paid in:

	True ✔	False ✔
Interest may be paid on the amount of the cheque after two working days		
The amount of the cheque may only be taken out of the bank after four working days		
The amount of the cheque may only be taken out of the bank after six working days		
The amount of the cheque paid in is only guaranteed and safe to be withdrawn out of the account after six working days		
The amount of the cheque paid in is only guaranteed and safe to be withdrawn out of the account after ten working days		

(b)

Link the forms of customer payment in the boxes on the left with the most appropriate statement on the right. There is one correct statement for each type of payment.

Cash		payments are made direct from the customer's bank to the supplier's bank
Credit card		payments are taken from the card-holder's bank immediately
Bank transfer (eg BACS)		payments are paid for by the card-holder at a later date
Debit card		should be banked as soon as possible and kept in a safe overnight
Cheques		reach the recipient's bank account at the end of each month
		payments take seven days to reach the recipient's bank account
		should be checked to ensure that they are signed

(c)

A supermarket till taking payment from a customer using a 'chip and PIN' credit or debit card must **always**:

	True ✔	False ✔
Obtain the customer's signature		
Avoid reading the PIN number of the card as it is entered		
Obtain authorisation over the telephone if the amount of the transaction is over the store 'floor limit'		

for your notes

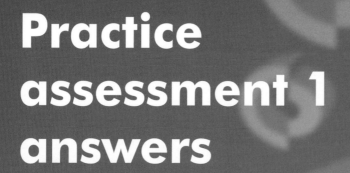

Practice
assessment 1
answers

Task 1

Account name	Amount £	Debit	Credit
Cash	250	✔	
Bank overdraft	2,359		✔
Vehicles	12,500	✔	
Machinery	8,400	✔	
Capital	25,410		✔
Inventory	3,987	✔	
Sales ledger control	4,381	✔	
Purchases ledger control	3,326		✔
Rent and rates	1,085	✔	
Miscellaneous expenses	492	✔	
Journal to record the opening entries of the new business			

Task 2

(a)

Account name	Amount £	Debit	Credit
Wages expense	40,827	✔	
Wages control	40,827		✔

(b)

Account name	Amount £	Debit	Credit
Wages control	11,480	✔	
HM Revenue & Customs	11,480		✔

(c)

Account name	Amount £	Debit	Credit
Wages control	25,867	✔	
Bank	25,867		✔

(d)

Account name	Amount £	Debit	Credit
Wages control	3,480	✔	
Pension fund	3,480		✔

Task 3

(a)

Account name	Amount £	Debit	Credit
Irrecoverable debts	920	✔	
Value Added Tax	184	✔	
Sales ledger control	1,104		✔

(b)

Error in the general ledger	Error disclosed by the trial balance	Error NOT disclosed by the trial balance
Commission received of £150 has been credited to rent received account		✔
Sales returns of £225 have been credited to sales account	✔	
A bank payment for vehicle repairs has been recorded in the cash book only	✔	
The balance of sales account has been calculated incorrectly	✔	

(c)

	Error of omission	Error of original entry	Error of commission
Discount received of £72 has been recorded in the discount received account as £27		✔	
A bank payment to a credit supplier has not been entered in the cash book or the purchases ledger control account	✔		
A sales invoice for £340 for Playwell Ltd has been debited to the account of Playtime Ltd			✔

Task 4

(a)

Account name	Amount £	Debit	Credit
Bank	690	✔	
Rates	690		✔

(b)

Account name	Amount £	Debit	Credit
Rates	609	✔	
Bank	609		✔

Task 5

(a)

(1)

Account name	Amount £	Debit	Credit
Purchases ledger control	4,760	✔	

(2)

Account name	Amount £	Debit	Credit
Purchases ledger control	5,760		✔

(3)

Account name	Amount £	Debit	Credit
Suspense	1,000	✔	

(b)

(1)

Account name	Amount £	Debit	Credit
Bank	220	✔	
Commission received	220		✔

(2)

Account name	Amount £	Debit	Credit
Bank	220	✔	
Commission received	220		✔

Task 6

Rent received Account

Details	Amount £	Details	Amount £
Rent paid	450		

Rent paid Account

Details	Amount £	Details	Amount £
		Rent received	450

Purchases Account

Details	Amount £	Details	Amount £
Suspense	500		

Suspense Account

Details	Amount £	Details	Amount £
Balance b/f	625	Purchases	500
		Office expenses	125

Office expenses Account

Details	Amount £	Details	Amount £
Suspense	125		

Task 7

Account name	Balances extracted on 30 June £	Balances at 1 July	
		Debit £	Credit £
Vehicles	17,800	17,800	
Inventory	4,925	4,925	
Sales ledger control	6,318	6,318	
Petty cash control	49	49	
Capital	18,835		18,835
Loan from bank	3,841		3,841
VAT owing to HM Revenue & Customs	1,596		1,596
Purchases ledger control	4,389		4,389
Bank overdraft	1,497		2,057
Sales	86,833		86,833
Sales returns	2,076	2,436	
Purchases	41,783	41,783	
Purchases returns	1,086		1,086
Wages	33,965	33,965	
Advertising	3,864	3,864	
Insurance	1,597	1,597	
Heating and lighting	1,326	1,326	
Rent and rates	2,847	2,847	
Vehicle expenses	1,727	1,727	
Suspense account (credit balance)	200	–	–
Totals		118,637	118,637

Task 8

(a) – (c)

CASH BOOK

Date 20-4	Details	Bank £	Date 20-4	Cheque number	Details	Bank £
01 Jun	Balance b/f	1,487	01 Jun	114117	Hendric & Co	395
04 Jun	Cottle Ltd	4,806	01 Jun	114118	Harrup & Noyes	1,310
20 Jun	W Waugh	2,108	10 Jun	114119	Farr Ltd	2,218
24 Jun	Pardo Ltd	1,746	18 Jun	114120	Bradnock Trading	1,036
24 Jun	Torre & Co	542	18 Jun	114121	Paxtons	1,427
21 Jun	Bayer Ltd	1,095	18 Jun	114122	Filiaps Ltd	798
21 Jun	Allen plc	2,786	20 Jun		Wyvern Council	235
			22 Jun		JA Finance	592
			24 Jun		Bank charges	45
			25 Jun		Balance c/d	6,514
		14,570				14,570
26 Jun	Balance b/d	6,514				

Task 9

(a)

Bank reconciliation statement as at 30 September 20-4	
Balance as per bank statement	£2,491
Add:	
Name: W Waugh	£946
Total to add	£946
Less:	
Name: O Borne	£760
Name: Filiaps	£1,055
Total to subtract	£1,815
Balance as per cash book	£1,622

(b)

It is important to reconcile the cash book to the | bank statement |
on a | regular | basis.

The bank statement provides an | independent | accounting record
and helps to prevent | fraud | .

It also highlights any | timing | differences and explains
why there is a | discrepancy | between the bank statement
balance and the | cash book | balance.

Task 10

(a)

Details	Amount	Debit	Credit
	£		
Balance of credit suppliers at 1 June	18,392		✔
Goods bought on credit	6,874		✔
Payments made to credit suppliers	8,937	✔	
Discounts received	154	✔	
Goods returned to credit suppliers	529	✔	

(b)

Cr £15,646	✔

(c)

	£
Balance on purchases ledger control account at 30 June	15,646
Total of the purchases ledger balances at 30 June	16,231
Difference	585

(d)

An invoice was entered twice in the purchases ledger	✔

(e)

Reconciliation of the purchases ledger control account assures managers that the amount showing as outstanding to suppliers is correct	✔
Reconciliation of the purchases ledger control account highlights any differences between the subsidiary ledger total and the control account balance	✔

Task 11

(a)

VAT control Account

Details	Amount £	Details	Amount £
Purchases	9,080	Balance b/f	9,804
Sales returns	368	Sales	14,800
Petty cash	17	Purchases returns	248
Irrecoverable debt	108	Cash sales	376
Computer equipment	575		
Bank	9,804		

(b)

Yes	✔
No	

(c)

	True	False
The VAT control account is used to calculate how much VAT is due to, or sometimes from, HMRC	✔	
A debit balance on the VAT control account indicates that the business is due a refund from HMRC	✔	
A bank payment of VAT due to HMRC will be entered as a debit in the VAT control account	✔	

Task 12

(a)

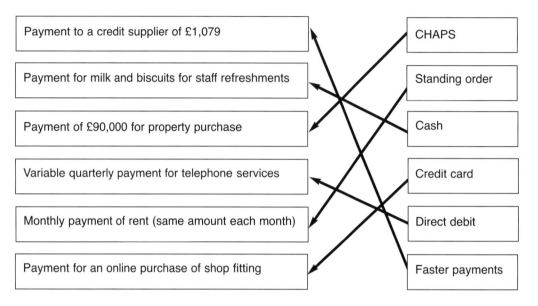

Payment to a credit supplier of £1,079	CHAPS
Payment for milk and biscuits for staff refreshments	Standing order
Payment of £90,000 for property purchase	Cash
Variable quarterly payment for telephone services	Credit card
Monthly payment of rent (same amount each month)	Direct debit
Payment for an online purchase of shop fitting	Faster payments

(b)

	True	False
Building societies offer banking services predominantly to individuals whereas banks offer banking services to both individuals and businesses	✔	
A bank draft is signed by a business customer to authorise a direct debit payment		✔
If the business has an overdraft, the bank owes the business money		✔

(c)

A business should have a banking document | retention | policy.

The length of time records should be kept is | variable | according to the type of record.

After this period of time the document should be | shredded | .

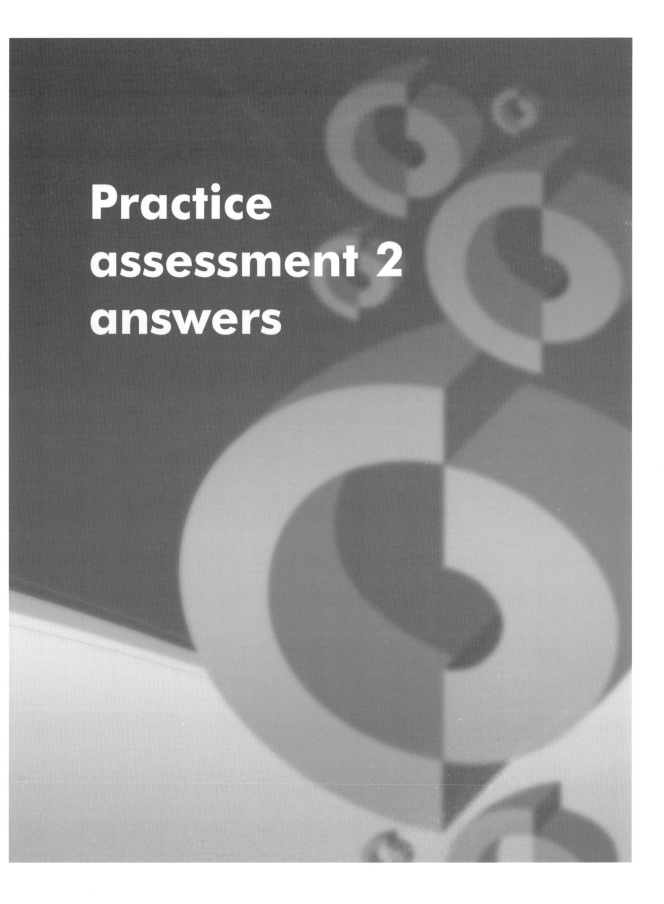

Practice assessment 2 answers

Task 1

Account name	Amount £	Debit	Credit
Cash	150	✔	
Cash at bank	12,350	✔	
Capital	23,456		✔
Fixtures and fittings	2,100	✔	
Insurance	825	✔	
Loan from bank	10,000		✔
Miscellaneous expenses	218	✔	
Motor vehicle	15,650	✔	
Office expenses	613	✔	
Rent and rates	1,550	✔	
Journal to record the opening entries of new business			

Task 2

(a)

Account name	Amount £	Debit	Credit
Wages expense	6,966	✔	
Wages control	6,966		✔

(b)

Account name	Amount £	Debit	Credit
HM Revenue & Customs	3,158		✔
Wages control	3,158	✔	

(c)

Account name	Amount £	Debit	Credit
Bank	3,508		✔
Wages control	3,508	✔	

(d)

Account name	Amount £	Debit	Credit
Trade Union	300		✔
Wages control	300	✔	

Task 3

(a)

Account name	Amount £	Debit	Credit
Irrecoverable debts	1,560	✔	
VAT	312	✔	
Sales ledger control	1,872		✔

(b)

Error in the general ledger	Error disclosed by the trial balance	Error NOT disclosed by the trial balance
Recording a bank payment for heat and light on the debit side of both the bank and heat and light account	✔	
Incorrectly calculating the balance on the rent account	✔	
Recording a payment by cheque to a creditor in the bank account and purchases ledger only	✔	
Recording a bank payment of £470 for motor repairs as £4700 in both accounts		✔

(c)

	Reversal of entries	Error of original entry	Error of principle
Recording a payment for motor repairs in the motor vehicles account			✔
Recording a sales credit note on the debit side of the sales ledger control account and the credit side of the sales returns account	✔		
Recording a bank payment for a telephone bill as £249 in both accounts when the actual bill was for £294		✔	

Task 4

(a)

Account name	Amount £	Debit	Credit
Bank	1,520	✔	
Rent paid	1,520		✔

(b)

Account name	Amount £	Debit	Credit
Rent paid	1,250	✔	
Bank	1,250		✔

Task 5

(a)

(1)

Account name	Amount £	Debit	Credit
VAT	1,100		✔

(2)

Account name	Amount £	Debit	Credit
VAT	1,000	✔	

(3)

Account name	Amount £	Debit	Credit
Suspense	100	✔	

(b)

(1)

Account name	Amount £	Debit	Credit
Heat and light	350	✔	
Bank	350		✔

(2)

Account name	Amount £	Debit	Credit
Heat and light	350	✔	
Bank	350		✔

Task 6

(a)

Office stationery Account

Details	Amount £	Details	Amount £
Suspense	167		

Rent and rates Account

Details	Amount £	Details	Amount £
		Suspense	1,800

Suspense Account

Details	Amount £	Details	Amount £
Rent and rates	1,800	Balance b/f	1,633
		Office stationery	167

Bank interest received Account

Details	Amount £	Details	Amount £
Bank interest charged	98		

Bank interest charged Account

Details	Amount £	Details	Amount £
		Bank interest received	98

Task 7

	Balances extracted on 30 June	Balances at 1 July	
	£	Debit £	Credit £
Motor vehicles	34,536	34,536	
Fixtures and fittings	17,350	17,350	
Inventory	7,300	7,300	
Bank overdraft	5,521	5,521	
Petty cash	100	100	
Sales ledger control	100,625	100,625	
Purchases ledger control	56,119		56,119
VAT owing to HM Revenue & Customs	8,300		8,300
Capital	22,844		22,844
Sales	222,955		222,955
Purchases	112,250	112,250	
Purchases returns	6,780		6,870
Wages	25,700	25,700	
Motor expenses	1,368	1,368	
Office expenses	3,354	3,354	
Rent and rates	1,444	1,444	
Heat and light	2,155	2,155	
Insurance	3,165	3,165	
Miscellaneous expenses	2,220	2,220	
Suspense account (debit balance)	10,952		
Totals		**317,088**	**317,088**

Task 8

(a) to (c)

Cash book as at 23 June

Date 20-4	Details	Bank £	Date 20-4	Cheque number	Details	Bank £
01 June	Balance b/f	15,189	01 June	111042	Prime kitchens	10,000
16 June	Britten & Bond	175	01 June	111043	Equipdirect	1,420
20 June	Macklin Ltd	950	01 June	111044	Long and Lane	80
21 June	Randle fitments	300	01 June	111045	BLH Ltd	795
12 June	Cabot and Co	571	02 June	111046	MVR Ltd	652
			02 June	111047	Fairfield Ltd	2,500
			13 June	111048	Makin and King	450
			13 June		LBMC	150
			20 June		Insurance Direct	850
			23 June		Bank charges	88
			23 June		Overdraft fees	30
			23 June		Balance c/d	170
		17,185				17,185
24 June	Balance b/d	170				

Task 9

(a)

Bank reconciliation statement as at 30 September 20-4	
Balance as per bank statement	£752
Add:	
Name: Barber Bates Ltd	£469
Total to add	£469
Less:	
Name: Bridge Tools	£607
Name: Tenon Ltd	£1,505
Total to subtract	£2,112
Balance as per cash book	£891

(b)

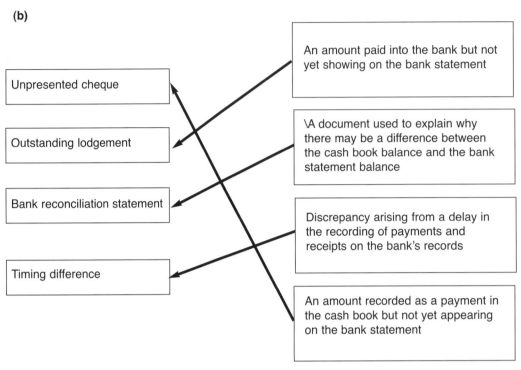

Task 10

(a)

Details	Amount £	Debit	Credit
Balance of creditors at 1 June	50,530		✔
Goods bought on credit	17,504		✔
Payments made to credit suppliers	20,672	✔	
Discount received	392	✔	
Goods returned to credit suppliers	784	✔	

(b)

Cr £46,186	✔

(c)

	£
Purchases ledger control account balance as at 30 June	46,186
Total of subsidiary (purchases) ledger accounts as at 30 June	45,794
Difference	392

(d)

Goods returned may have been entered in the subsidiary ledger twice	✔

(e)

	True	False
Reconciliation of the sales ledger control account assures managers that the amount showing as outstanding from customers is correct	✔	
The balance of the sales ledger control account should agree to the total of the balances in the sales ledger	✔	
The balance of the sales ledger control account should agree to the total of the aged trade payables analysis		✔
Reconciliation of the sales ledger control account highlights any differences between the subsidiary ledger total and the control account balance	✔	

Task 11

(a)

VAT control account

Details	Amount £	Details	Amount £
Purchases	19,600	Balance b/f	4,666
Sales returns	560	Sales	34,400
Petty cash	11	Purchases returns	1,520
Irrecoverable debt	96	Cash sales	64
Office equipment	420		
Bank	4,666		

(b)

Yes	
No	✔

(c)

	True	False
VAT totals from the day books are posted to the VAT control account	✔	
A credit balance on the VAT control account indicates that the business owes money to HMRC	✔	
A refund of VAT from HMRC will be entered as a debit in the VAT control account		✔

Task 12

(a)

Checks to be made	Cheque	Telephone credit card payment
Check expiry date		✔
Check issue number		
Check not post-dated	✔	
Check security number		✔
Check words and figures match	✔	
Check card has not been tampered with		

(b)

	True	False
When Cucina Ltd makes payments to suppliers by credit card, the amount leaves the bank current account immediately		✔
When Cucina Ltd makes payments to suppliers by debit card, the amount paid does not affect the bank current account		✔

(c)

Aged trade receivable analysis	
Aged trade payable analysis	
Bank statements	✔
Credit cards	
Debit cards	
Paying in slip stubs	✔
Remittance advice notes	
Supplier invoices	

Practice assessment 3 answers

Task 1

Account name	Amount £	Debit	Credit
Capital	5,000		✔
Bank loan	6,000		✔
Computer equipment	2,622	✔	
Inventory	3,178	✔	
Trade payables	3,814		✔
Bank (debit balance)	5,984	✔	
Cash	239	✔	
Discounts received	32		✔
Premises expenses	2,187	✔	
VAT (debit balance)	636	✔	

Task 2

(a)

Account name	Amount £	Debit	Credit
Wages expense	50,176	✔	
Wages control	50,176		✔

(b)

Account name	Amount £	Debit	Credit
Wages control	36,864	✔	
Bank	36,864		✔

Task 3

(a)

Errors	Error disclosed by the trial balance	Error NOT disclosed by the trial balance
A cash purchase has been entered in the cash book but not in the purchases account	✔	
Discount allowed of £98 has been recorded in the discount allowed account as £89	✔	
A receipt from a credit customer has not been entered in the cash book or the sales ledger control account		✔
A purchase credit note for £296 has been debited to the purchases account and credited to the purchases ledger control account		✔

(b)

	Error of principle	Compensating error	Error of commission
The purchase of studio recording equipment for £3,000 has been debited to the recording expense account	✔		
The sales account has been overcast by £10. The purchases account has also been overcast by £10		✔	
A purchase invoice for £235 for Stage Supplies Ltd has been credited to the account of Stage Equipment Ltd			✔

(c)

Account name	Amount £	Debit	Credit
Irrecoverable debts	110	✔	
VAT	22	✔	
Sales ledger control	132		✔

Task 4

(a)

Account name	Amount £	Debit	Credit
Bank	4,321	✔	
Recording equipment	4,321		✔

(b)

Account name	Amount £	Debit	Credit
Recording equipment	3,421	✔	
Bank	3,421		✔

Task 5

(a)

Account name	Amount £	Debit	Credit
Suspense	192		✔

(b)

Account name	Amount £	Debit	Credit
VAT	192		✔

(c)

Account name	Amount £	Debit	Credit
Suspense	192	✔	

(d)

Bank loan repayment	
Irrecoverable debt write off	✔
Opening entries at start of business	✔
Payment of VAT owing to HMRC	
Payroll transactions	✔
Purchase of non-current assets	✔
Transfer of cash from cash sales to bank	

Task 6

Sales Account

Details	Amount £	Details	Amount £
Suspense	99		

VAT Account

Details	Amount £	Details	Amount £
		Suspense	1,612

Bank interest paid Account

Details	Amount £	Details	Amount £
Bank charges	52		

Bank charges Account

Details	Amount £	Details	Amount £
		Bank interest paid	52

Suspense Account

Details	Amount £	Details	Amount £
VAT	1,612	Balance b/f	1,513
		Sales	99

Task 7

Account name	Amount £	Debit	Credit
Capital	25,672		✔
Bank loan	12,000		✔
Computer equipment	10,024	✔	
Recording equipment	5,412	✔	
Inventory	2,555	✔	
Purchases ledger control	2,299		✔
Bank overdraft	1,199		✔
Cash	250	✔	
Discounts allowed	297	✔	
Discounts received	105		✔
Premises expenses	2,187	✔	
VAT owing to HMRC	3,647		✔
Sales	62,988		✔
Purchases	35,212	✔	
Sales ledger control	7,298	✔	
Administration expenses	3,611	✔	
Wages	41,064	✔	
Suspense	0		

Task 8

(a) to (c)

Date 20-4	Details	Amount £	Date 20-4	Cheque number	Details	Amount £
04 Jul	Carpenter Ltd	3,170	01 Jul		Balance b/f	1,736
13 Jul	C King	2,563	01 Jul	100151	Arma Trading	862
25 Jul	A Murray	2,943	06 Jul	100153	K Bush	168
20 Jul	Ciccone	2,047	07 Jul	100152	Hynde Music	785
			10 Jul	SO	Telephone	110
			13 Jul	100154	Lennox & Co	129
			24 Jul	BACS	A Adkins	1,005
			31 Jul	BACS	Wages	5,236
			20 Jul	DD	Electricity	520
			28 Jul		Credit charges	62
			31 Jul		Balance c/d	110
		10,723				10,723
1 Aug	Balance b/d	110				

Task 9

(a)

Bank reconciliation statement as at 30 September 20-4	
Balance as per bank statement	£965
Add:	
Name: Winehouse Ltd	£411
Name: Twain Trading	£676
Total to add	£1,087
Less:	
Name: E Harris	£600
Name: N Simone	£342
Total to subtract	£942
Balance as per cash book	£1,110

(b)

The bank reconciliation explains any difference between the

balance in the cash book and the balance at the

bank .

It highlights any errors and

timing differences .

Access to bank records should be restricted to authorised

employees to safeguard the security of payments and

receipts.

Task 10

(a)

Sales ledger control account

Details	Amount	Debit	Credit
	£		
Balance owing from credit customers at 1 July	7,298	✔	
Money received from credit customers	6,450		✔
Discounts allowed	75		✔
Goods sold to credit customers	14,774	✔	
Goods returned by credit customers	501		✔
Journal credit to correct an error	89		✔

(b)

Purchases ledger control account

Details	Amount	Debit	Credit
	£		
Balance owing to credit suppliers at 1 July	2,299		✔
Money paid to credit suppliers	2,276	✔	
Discounts received	23	✔	
Goods purchased from credit suppliers	5,113		✔
Goods returned to credit suppliers	108	✔	

(c)

Debit balance of £9061	✔

(d)

	True	False
If an irrecoverable debt is not written off in the sales ledger control account, the balance on the account will be lower than it should be		✔
The balance of the purchases ledger control account should agree to the total of the aged trade payables analysis	✔	
Reconciliation of the sales ledger control account highlights any differences between the subsidiary ledger total and the control account balance	✔	

Task 11

(a)

VAT control account

Details	Amount £	Details	Amount £
Sales returns	280	Balance b/f	6,536
Purchases	9,800	Sales	17,200
Petty cash	9	Purchases returns	760
Irrecoverable debts	82	Sales	192
Studio equipment	400		
Bank	6,536		

The VAT Return has been completed and shows an amount owing to HMRC of £7581.

(b)

Yes	✔
No	

(c)

	True	False
VAT on purchases and expenses can only be entered in the VAT account if the purchase document bears the VAT registration number of the supplier	✔	
A bank receipt of a refund of VAT from HMRC would be shown as a credit in the VAT control account	✔	
A bank payment of VAT due to HMRC will be entered as a credit in the VAT control account	✔	

Task 12

(a)

	True	False
Interest may be paid on the amount of the cheque after two working days	✔	
The amount of the cheque may only be taken out of the bank after four working days	✔	
The amount of the cheque may only be taken out of the bank after six working days		✔
The amount of the cheque paid in is only guaranteed and safe to be withdrawn out of the account after six working days	✔	
The amount of the cheque paid in is only guaranteed and safe to be withdrawn out of the account after ten working days		✔

(b)

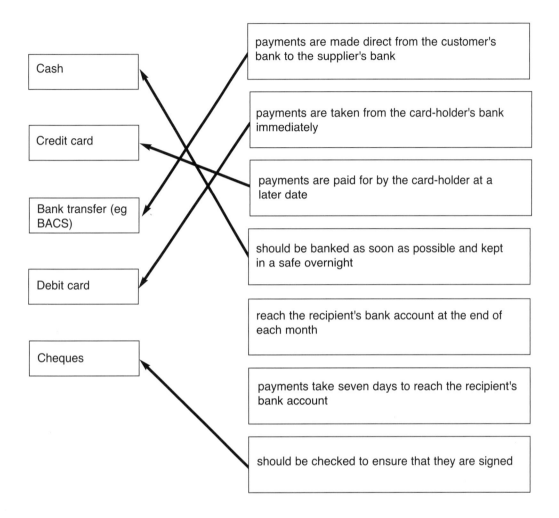

(c)

	True	False
Obtain the customer's signature		✔
Avoid reading the PIN number of the card as it is entered	✔	
Obtain authorisation over the telephone if the amount of the transaction is over the store 'floor limit'		✔

for your notes